Carnac

The Alignments

When Art and Science were One
Volume 1

Howard Crowhurst

 epistemea

2012

Books in English published by Epistemea

Back to Square One, Howard Crowhurst, April 2011

The Nebra Sky Disc, Cycles in the cosmos, Howard Crowhurst, December 2012

Books in French published by Epistemea (previously HCom):

Mémoire de Pierres à Plouharnel, Howard Crowhurst et Philippe Gaillard, 2004

Mégalithes, Principes de la première architecture monumentale du monde,
Howard Crowhurst , 2007, réédition 2010.

Carnac, Les Alignements, Quand l'Art et la Science ne faisaient qu'un.
Howard Crowhurst , 2010.

Second edition (first edition April 2011)
Copyright © EPISTEMEA, 2012
Copyright © for photographs et diagrams, Howard Crowhurst, 2010, except photos 11, 12 et 22.
Cover (photo and design) : Howard Crowhurst

ISBN : 978-2-9521871-6-9

For any information or orders, please visit our website www.epistemea.com
or contact
EPISTEMEA
4 avenue de l'océan
56340 PLOUHARNEL
contact@epistemea.com

Carnac

The Alignments

Contents

Introduction   5

Chapter 1: Le Menec   9

   Western beginning   9

   Le Menec – General description   23

   Le Menec – Eastern alignments   27

   Le Menec East Cromlech   29

   Le Menec – General plan   33

Chapter 2 : Megalithic Landscaping   35

   The Tumulus Saint Michel, Le Menec West and East relationship.   41

   The monuments of the Boyne Valley, Ireland.   49

Chapter 3 : Three parts of a whole   53

   Le Menec –Kermario   53

   The Kermario Alignments   57

   Le Manio 2   79

   Kerlescan   83

   Le Petit Menec   97

Conclusion   117

Acknowledgements   119

Appendices and Tables   120

Bibliography   126

Photo 1: The beginning of the Le Menec alignments

Photo 2 : Kermario alignments viewed from the north east towards the beginning with the Tumulus Saint Michel, topped by its chapel, on the left horizon.

The Carnac Alignments

Introduction

The Carnac alignments are probably the most mysterious of all the prehistoric monuments in the world. At the time of writing (September 2010), there is no "official" theory whatsoever concerning the purpose of these rows of granite standing stones, over 3000 in number, which march for four kilometres across the countryside of southern Brittany in France. In addition, few people realise that, although they are gigantic, these stones are only a small part of an enormous "complex" of major megalithic monuments covering an area of around 200 square kilometres, built from 6000BCE onwards, making some monuments at least 2000 years older than the most ancient sites in Great Britain.

In nearby Locmariaquer lies the Grand Menhir Brisé, the world's largest ever megalith, weighing in at around 330 tons and over 20 metres long. It is made of ortho-gneiss, a kind of granite which is only to be found over 10 kilometres away. To quote Jean-Pierre Mohen, director of French antiquities and leading megalithic specialist, "There is no serious hypothesis which explains how these massive stones could have been transported."[1]

However, perhaps the biggest mystery of all, and archaeologically the most embarrassing, is that despite the self-evident need for large numbers of people to erect these monuments, very few traces of Neolithic human dwelling places are to be found. If the builders were locals, perhaps their dwellings now lie under the sea. If they were visitors, then they cleared up their picnics before leaving.

As the classical approaches give very few answers, what can be said about Carnac?

These alignments are an amazing remnant of a forgotten civilisation which disappeared so long ago that we have no record of it ever having existed. The stones, however, tell a story, even if many thousands have disappeared, and they tell it in the language of geometry and measurement.

A more detailed study of the Carnac alignments brings to light an intentional organisation which is simply unbelievable.[a2] The aim of this present work is to show how the Carnac alignments were organised, what they reveal to us and why they are where they are, not only from a local but also a global view point.

---

[a]This study goes much further into the details of the Carnac alignments than in my first book.

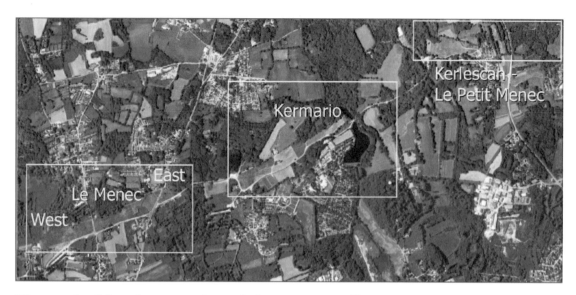

Figure 1 : The three series of the Carnac alignments.

Photo 3 : Kerlescan alignments at spring equinox sunrise

Ever since the nineteenth century, when the major activity of many scientists consisted of putting things into categories, the Carnac stone alignments have been described as three "series". From West to East, which seems to be the direction intended, they are named Le Menec, Kermario and Kerlescan - Le Petit Menec. The final series, divided into two parts by the Auray to La Trinité main road, lies astride two towns and so has two names. This, of course, is in no way linked to the builder's initial plans, although it may affect the way we "moderns" look at it. There are gaps in between each series and the directions they take are different. However, they have several things in common which appear even from a superficial observation.

1. The size and shape of the stones.
The largest stones, which can be over four metres tall, are to be found to the west of each section. They get progressively smaller as one goes towards the east until they finally fade out. There are exceptions to this rule, as we sometimes suddenly come across a menhir, the French word for standing stone, which is far taller than those surrounding it. According to geological work on granite erosion by Dominique Sellier[3], these "giants" may be much older then their neighbours. Another difference is that the stones get bigger at the eastern end of the Le Menec rows. All the stones are roughly quarried, and although certain shapes recur, none are identical. They resemble the stones at Avebury in Great Britain but not at all those at Stonehenge.

2. The plateau and cromlech.
A flat area on slightly higher ground with visible bedrock is to be found at the start of all three series. The lines of stones start at the plateau's eastern limit and go westwards down a slope. At Le Menec and Kerlescan, this departure point is marked by menhirs which are perpendicular to the rows and touch each other. They are part of a stone structure, known as a cromlech which encloses the plateau. There are few signs of this structure at the head of the Kermario alignments, although some very large recumbent stones are to be found to the north west. According to Félix Gaillard[4], a nineteenth century antiquarian, it may have been destroyed by the Romans who left many remains on the site.

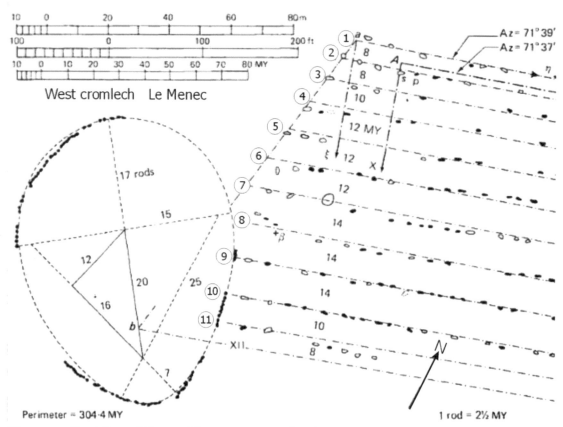

Figure 2: The West Menec cromlech and the beginning of the alignments (Alexander Thom)

Photo 4 : The north west side of the Le Menec Cromlech.

3. The number of lines and the Table stones.

It is impossible to say with certainty exactly how many lines were initially erected in the different parts of the Carnac alignments. At Le Menec, Professor Thom[5] counted 12 lines (Figure 2), but the most southerly line is questionable as there is no sign of it at the beginning. Gaillard, who knew Le Menec before any restoration work took place and also before many of the constructions in the village were built, ascertains the existence of eleven lines. Kermario is composed of ten rows at present and this is the number given by James Miln[6] while Kerlescan counts eleven although Gaillard suggests thirteen. What can be affirmed is that these three series of alignments have approximately the same number of lines. Work by Cassen[7] has shown the existence of at least twenty lines in the Saint Pierre Quiberon site, now partly under the sea, and Gaillard surmises an original fifty lines at Kerzerho, Erdeven.

A massive flat recumbent stone, called the Table Stone, can be found near the centre of the beginning of the Le Menec (row 7) and Kermario (row 6) sites.

4. A general direction.

Although the stone rows are not perfectly straight lines and the different series are not aiming towards exactly the same orientation, they do seem to be organised around a central axis which is approximately 4 kilometres long. The stones at Le Petit Menec are different because they change direction several times, giving the impression of following the arc of a circle. Before looking closer at the overall picture, it is first necessary to detail the particularities of each section and to consider two major monuments which are related to them, the Tumulus Saint Michel and the Tumulus de Kercado.

Chapter 1: Le Menec

Western beginning

This is the most well known part of the Carnac alignments, being closest to the town and possessing a large car park, tourist information centre and bookshop. The general public have free access between the end of October and the end of March. During the summer season however, it is only available by paying for and following an official guided tour which lasts about an hour. It is possible to visit the cromlech (Photo 4) all year round, as it totally intermingles with the houses in the Le Menec village. It is an incredible survivor of urbanisation and although there are gaps, 71 stones

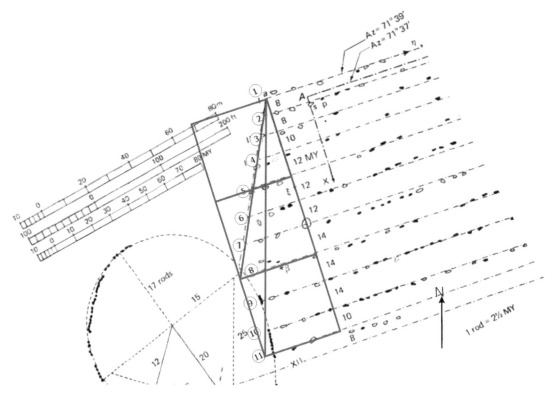

Figure 3: The diagonal of a double square traces the start of the rows at Le Menec West. The diagonal of the triple square is due North-South.

Photo 5 : The Table Stone at Le Menec

which touch each other clearly reveal the initial shape of the construction. Professor Thom classified it as a type-1 egg (Figure 2), a design based on two 3-4-5 triangles placed back to back, the shape of many stone "circles" in Britain[8]. He also suggested the use of the megalithic yard (0.829m) as the fundamental measurement of the megalith builders, a distance he arrived at after over 20 years of high precision surveying and the use of a statistical method designed by the major experts of the time[9]. Unfortunately for Thom, if findings undermine existing paradigms, then many people will simply not believe them, even if they are proved to be correct. My own work entirely corroborates the use of the megalithic yard, and its 2.5 multiple, the megalithic rod (mr), in the Carnac monuments, although I do not believe it was the only unit of measurement employed.

Now Thom had noticed that the first menhirs in the rows 1 to 5 were at a particular angle with respect to the rows themselves, line "a" to "b" on his diagram, and that this alignment was continued along the lines. In other words, if you see how the stones align when you look across the rows, this particular angle is constantly repeated, stone after stone for hundreds of metres. Thom's survey showed this to be a 1 to 2 angle, that is 63.435°, the angle of the diagonal of a double square, but he went no further with this line of research.

My previous work on ancient sacred architecture had shown to me the importance of the double square in Egypt and Mesopotamia[2]. It is the symbolic representation of the number 2 and duality, the basis of creation on the human level. It is often to be found combined with the triple square showing the junction of the square (unity-cosmic creator) with the double square (duality–mankind). A very good example of this is the ground plan of Solomon's Temple, dictated by God himself according to the Old Testament. It is a triple square, 20 cubits wide and 60 cubits long composed of the square holy of holies (20 by 20) and the double square temple (20 by 40).

As soon as I positioned a double square on the beginning of the Le Menec lines, a geometrical design appeared. Thom had measured the distances between the rows in megalithic yards (my). The sum of the measurements between rows 1 and 5 is 38 my, (8+8+10+12). This is equal to the sum between rows 5 and 8 (12+12+14). So the diagonal of a double square positioned at right angles to the axis of the alignments traces the beginning of the first five rows and splits the first eight rows into two equally measured groups, the first having four intervals and the second three (Figure 3 and Appendix 2).

Furthermore, rows 8 to 11 also add up to 38my (14+14+10), creating a perfect triple square, **whose diagonal is precisely orientated N-S**. It is

Photo 6 : The three E-W orientated stones at the start of row 8 position the base of the septuple square. (see figure 5 on page 14).

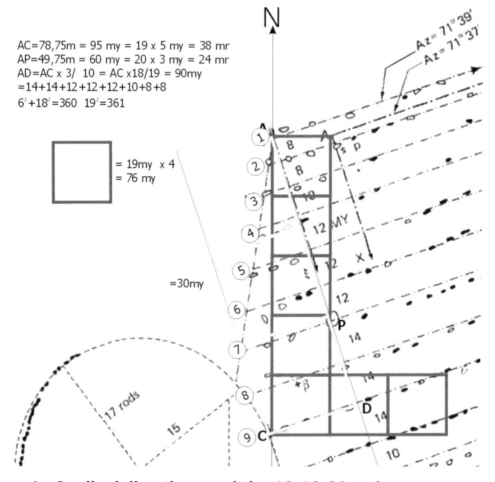

AC=78,75m = 95 my = 19 x 5 my = 38 mr
AP=49,75m = 60 my = 20 x 3 my = 24 mr
AD=AC x 3/ 10 = AC x18/19 = 90my
=14+14+12+12+12+10+8+8
$6^2+18^2=360$ $19^2=361$

= 19my x 4
= 76 my

=30my

17 rods

Figure 4 : Cardinal directions and the 18-19-20 ratio

important to point out that the number 38 found in connection with a triple square is immediately significant because a triple square with a side length of 36 units has a diagonal of 38 units to a very high precision (99.86%).

Thom had painstakingly recorded the angle that each row made with respect to the North (Table 1). Felix Gaillard re-erected about 70 stones here between 1884 and 1886. Fortunately, he took photographs and drew up detailed plans before beginning his restoration work. His task was continued by Zacharie Le Rouzic, who seems to have been less meticulous, but who introduced the principle of marking the re-erected menhirs with a small red indelible square, making it possible to ascertain on site the stones which have never moved since they were first put there over 6000 years ago. Professor Thom paid particular attention to this fact when he did his surveys, drafted his plans and made his conclusions concerning the geometrical principles underlying the monument's construction.

He apparently never noticed, however, that the angle of the Le Menec rows with respect to the East corresponds to the angle of a triple square, 18.435° (see Appendix 1). If we take the average of Thom's results for the first seven rows, we get this angle to within 5 thousandths of a degree, a higher precision than that given by Thom (Table 1). So the triple square covers eleven lines and ten intervals. Its side measures 114my divided into three parts of 38my. The right hand side goes through the centre of the Table Stone in row 7, 62my from the north and 52 my from the south.

The first three stones in row 8 attracted my attention as they were not at all in line with the others. In fact, I discovered them to be orientated along an East West line. This suggested some geometrical organisation with respect to the cardinal directions. Their position on the north south diagonal of the triple square gave weight to this hypothesis. In Figure 4, we see how the double square of 38 my has been turned and precisely positions the first three stones in row 8. It is divided into four squares with sides of 19my (in red). The first three red squares position the Table Stone (P). The distance AP is 19my times the square root of 10 which gives 60.08my (Appendix 1). By adding a fifth red square, row 9 is accurately placed and then its direction is determined by the horizontal triple square. The line AC from row 1 to row 9 measures 5 times 19my, that is 95 my or 38mr. AD, the perpendicular distance between rows 1 to 9, can be found by adding Thom's measurements, written on his plan, 8+8+10+12+12+12+14+14=90my. Now 90 = 95 x 18/19. This obviously suggests another triple square, added in yellow, with a side of 30my. It positions the Table Stone and also rows 4 and 9.

We can calculate AC, its diagonal, by multiplying AD by the square root of

Figure 5 : The double square, the triple square and the septuple square combine in the West Menec geometry

Photo 7 : Group of 9 touching stones on the east side of the Le Menec West cromlech. The two menhirs in the foreground are the first stones of the 10th and 11th rows.

10. This gives 94.86my, a difference of only 11 centimetres with respect to the geometry of the red 19my squares. This difference is obviously absorbed by the size of the stones.

My study on the Tumulus Saint Michel, which we will examine shortly, had brought to light an extraordinary geometrical fact. The angle of the diagonal of a septuple square (8.13°) when added to that of a triple square (18.435°) gives the exact angle of the diagonal of a double square (26.565°). In Figure 5, I suggest how this geometry has been used at Le Menec West. The seven intervals between row 1 and row 8 are schematically represented by the septuple square, orientated again to incredibly precise cardinal directions, as shown by the satellite photo. It is aligned to the first three menhirs of row 8 . Its diagonal's position coincides with that of our first double square (Figure 3). This is shown by the identical double square in green in Figure 5 which has been turned so that its left hand side coincides with the septuple square's diagonal. The measurement given by the satellite imagery programme (in yellow) is 63 metres, which, converted into megalithic yards, (0.829m) gives 76my (38x2). So the side length of the septuple square is equal to that of the double square.

Much more astonishing, however, is the exact conversion between megalithic yards and metres. 63 metres is 7 times 9 metres, revealing that our 7 meridian orientated squares have sides exactly 9 metres long. I have already expressed my belief that the metre length was a secret measurement known long before the French revolution and revealed at that time for political reasons. Evidence of this is to be found in the well attested Drusian or Teutonic foot, examples of which were found to measure exactly 333 millimetres from the 13th century[10]. The definition given for the metre was the ten millionth part of one quarter of the Earth's meridian. This measurement could consequently have been known at any point in history, since it is universal. Its presence here on a perfect North-South line can hardly be a coincidence, although I expect many people will have difficulty accepting it.

A closer look at the interval between rows 8 and 11 supports this hypothesis. The north south distance between these rows is 36 metres, which can be traced using four 9m blue squares. This makes a total of 11 blue squares and gives a north-south width to the alignments of 99 metres. This is very close to the geometrical value calculated from the diagonal of the triple square (Appendix 2). 114my times the square root of 10 divided by 3 gives 120.16 my or 99.61 metres. Furthermore, Gaillard had noticed that the distance between the rows gets greater as one goes southwards and Thom confirmed this with the exception of rows 10 and 11. Here, the 9

Photo 8 : 3 touching stones in the cromlech perpendicular to the start of row 9. The triple squares are the same size.

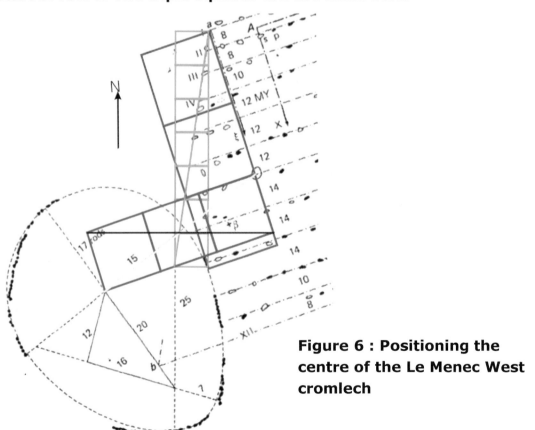

Figure 6 : Positioning the centre of the Le Menec West cromlech

metre square can be accurately placed with its corners on the first two stones of each row (Figure 5). Photo 7 shows how the space between these two rows is marked by **9 touching stones,** giving a numerical interpretation of the interval.

Thom spent much time completing the difficult task of exactly positioning the stones of the Le Menec West cromlech. Surveying must have been very difficult as visibility is greatly reduced by the buildings in the village. He was, however, a highly accomplished surveyor and produced an accurate plan, precisely locating the five stones which had never been moved. This enables us to go further into the understanding of the relationship between the cromlech or "Egg" and the stone rows. To do this, we must start by examining the beginning of row 9, where three stones of increasing size mark the point where the cromlech is exactly perpendicular to the alignments (Photo 8). The smaller stone on the left was added by Le Rouzic and is not visible on photos taken by Gaillard in the 19th century. The stone on the right has a flat top while the central one has an inclined upper edge, exactly at the angle of the diagonal of a triple square. These two stones have the same width and their respective heights have been perfectly adjusted as can be shown by the red squares. We shall later see that this same symbol is repeated at Le Menec East. The cromlech seems to stop here, as there is a gap until the most northerly point when the stones start heading south. The tallest of the three, which is slightly south of row 9, is due south of the beginning of row 1, the cornerstone of the whole plan.

We discover in Figure 6 that the line between these two points is the diagonal of yet another triple square (in red) with the Table Stone, two squares down the line perpendicular to the alignments drawn from point "a" at a distance of 62my. This gives the red triple square a size of 31my by 93my, a width 1 metre longer than the yellow square in Figure 4. The three touching stones in Photo 8 are aligned along its other side. The diagonal measures 98my to a precision of 99.97%, respecting again a whole number ratio despite a multiplication by the square root of 10. Moreover, if this same diagonal now becomes the side of a septuple square (in blue), where each square measures 14 my (14x7=98), the other side is precisely aligned on the right side of Thom's 3-4-5 triangle. The distance of 14my is the space between each row from rows 8 to 10.

The diagonal of this septuple square still runs along the beginning of the rows, but its bottom left corner positions a point. If we trace another triple square (in brown), turned by 90°, with its top right hand corner on the Table Stone, so that its bottom line goes through this point, its bottom left hand corner marks the exact centre of the half circle which forms the

Photo 9 : A road runs through the cromlech in the Le Menec village.

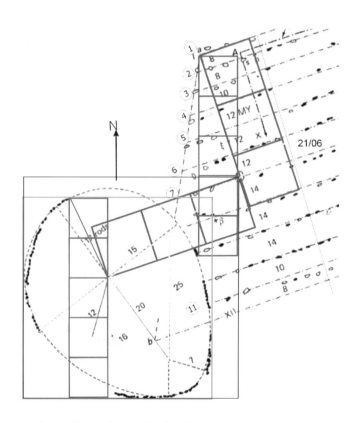

Figure 7 : Determining the size of the Le Menec West egg.

northern part of the egg and positions the two 3-4-5 triangles. Its sides measure 25 1/3rd my by 76 my which, as we have seen, is 4 times 19my. This clearly quadruple measurement along the three side of a triple square suggests the use of a 3-4-5 triangle and its yellow diagonal runs along the side of Thom's 3-4-5 triangle. The other diagonal, in black, is East-West and exactly crosses the septuple square between the sixth and seventh squares. The acute angle between the diagonals of a triple square is twice 18.435° which is 36.87°, the exact value of the smaller angle of a 3-4-5 triangle. The yellow diagonal, which joins the centre of the Egg to the Table Stone is consequently orientated at 36.87° north of East, which was the angle of summer solstice sunrise at this latitude at the neolithic period. It measures 76my times the square root of 10 divided by 3 which, as we have seen, is very close to 80my. As it is also the hypotenuse of a 3-4-5 triangle, the North-South distance between the centre of the egg and the Table Stone is 80 divided by 5 times 3 which is 48my.

Figure 7 shows how the North South size of the egg can be shown to be equal to the quintuple 19my square first seen in Figure 4. The centre of the egg seems to be positioned three squares up from the base and also two squares down and one square east from the most northerly stone in the perimeter. This is the same principle, but inverted, which placed the Table Stone between rows 1 and 9.

Professor Thom gives the radius of the north western circular section of the egg to be 17mr which is 42.5my. As this measurement is now suggested to be the diagonal of a double square, we can verify the size of the side of the square by dividing 42.5my by the square root of 5. The answer is **19.006my. This incredibly close result** would suggest that the builders knew an approximation of root 5 as being 38/17, precise to 99.97%. It would also imply that the northern section of the cromlech is not ruined but actually stopped exactly where it does now, which would appear to be confirmed by the stone itself, in archaeological terms a "blocking stone", implanted perpendicularly to the other menhirs (Photo 10).

The north-south distance between this stone and the Table Stone can be calculated to be 10my (48my-38my) and the total distance between the start of row 1 and the base of the cromlech to be 162my (19x8 +10). The whole of this organisation between the Table Stone and the cromlech is contained in a perfect square whose sides measure 105my.

The cromlech itself, however, is not surrounded by a perfect square but by a rectangle with a ratio of 18 to 19 (in blue) between its height and its width. The latter can be easily found from Thom's measurements. From the centre

Photo 10 : The most northerly stone in the Le Menec West egg, placed perpendicularly to the others to form a blocking stone.

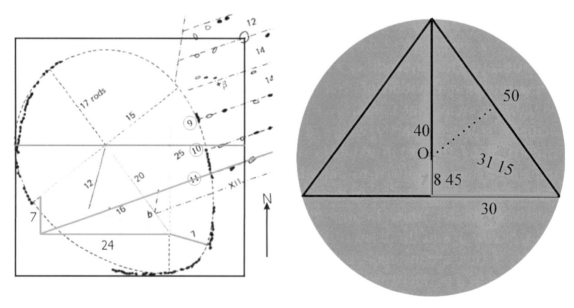

Figure 8 : The choice of 7mr and 25mr for tracing the Egg and a 5500 year-old Sumerian engraving.

to the western limit is 17mr. The yellow 3-4-5 gives the next horizontal section as 12mr and the last part is given by Thom as 7mr. This makes a total of 36mr or 90my. As the height of this blue rectangle is 95my and its width is 90my, we obtain the 18 to 19 ratio. This is an important confirmation of the preceding conclusions, underlining the essential role played by the triple square at Le Menec West. A series of relationships between square roots, centred around the number 19, is shown in Table 2.

A subtle geometrical element may still be added to this architectural masterpiece. As shown in Figure 8, another Pythagorean triangle may be included in Thom's plan, the 7-24-25. The two smaller angles of the 3-4-5 triangle (36.87°) when added make 73.74°. If this is subtracted from 90°, we obtain 16.26° which is the precise angle of the 7-24-25 triangle.

The 3-4-5 triangle is consequently the root triangle of the 7-24-25 triangle (see Figure 8). The 25 side measures 25 mr, showing how **this** triangle has given the Egg's dimensions. The south-east part of the Egg has been traced using this same length of 7mr. The east-west side is 24mr which is 60my, the same size as the two yellow squares in Figure 4. Finally, the right angled corner of this triangle is exactly on the axis of row 11, the most southerly row of the alignments in my opinion. We shall shortly discover the importance of this point.

Consequently, Professor Thom's 3-4-5 triangles are precisely orientated to the cardinal directions.

Figure 8 also shows a engraving found on a clay tablet in Mesopotamia, dated to the 3rd millennium BCE. It demonstrates the relationship between the 3-4-5 triangle, the 7-24-25 triangle and the circle, whose centre is at point O. The numbers in black were inscribed on the tablet in Sumerian number notation, which is base 60. When converted to decimal, 31 15 becomes 31.25 and 8 45 becomes 8.75. So we see how the summit of a 7-24-25 ratio triangle, added in green, drawn inside a 30-40-50 triangle, exactly positions the centre of a circle which goes through its corners and which has a diameter of 62.5 units (2 times 31.25).

Now 62.5my is equal to 25mr. So there is a geometrical and numerical relationship between the Sumerian diagram and the Carnac megalithic monument, obviously suggesting an ancient canon of thought common to both cultures. I pointed out in my previous work that 3.125 (as a fraction 25/8) was a practical approximation of Pi, still used in Roman times.

Photo 11 : An aerial view of the Le Menec alignments. Just after the white house, they turn north (left). The eastern rows can be seen in the distance. The Table Stone (lower central), has two people standing on it.

Le Menec – General description

After this spectacular beginning, the Le Menec alignments march off in more or less straight lines for 365 metres until they reach a road which has apparently been bulldozed through them. They continue on the other side for another 100 metres and then they turn towards the North (Photo 11). However, a previously unknown photograph taken by Felix Gaillard in 1880, discovered in 2003 by his descendants, (Photo 12), shows no trace of any menhirs on the eastern side of the road, in the foreground of the photo.

Photo 12 : Le Menec West alignments photographed in 1880 by Félix Gaillard before any restoration work had been started. The photograph was taken from the top of a slight slope, where today there is a white house (Photo 11). There is no sign of any menhirs, standing or ruined, in the foreground, where today seven dead straight lines of stones are to be found.

Plans drawn up in 1870 by Lukis and Dryden start at the top of the slope and leave a large blank space to the left where the present alignments should be. Could later "over-zealous" restoration work by Zacharie Le Rouzic have filled in the gaps? It could have been quite tempting. Local eye-witness accounts from people who were children in the 1920's suggest this actually happened but an archaeological excavation around the suspected add-ons would be necessary to scientifically confirm the idea. The central part of the Le Menec lines is rather chaotic, following which there is a complete gap in the rows before arriving at Le Menec East. Professor Thom was quite sure that there was a fairly simple geometrical pattern linking the sections, but I do not find his evidence convincing.

Photo 13 : The last part of the western section, between the road and the white house. These perfectly straight lines march up the sloping field in which no stones can be seen on Gaillard's photo from 1880 nor on Lukis and Dryden's plans from 1870.

Photo 14 : Le Menec central section in the foreground and eastern section in the distance. The different orientation of these two sections is clearly visible.

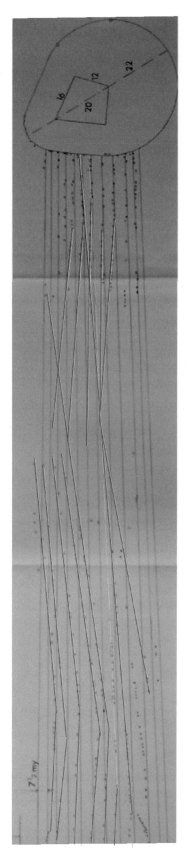

This is undoubtedly because he was not aware of this reorganisation of the last part of the western section.

In Figure 9, his plan suggests straight lines which link the western rows with those at the east.

I have added, in red, lines which actually follow the stones and which quite clearly are not aiming at the eastern cromlech. Were they to continue, they would pass to its north. This can also be seen in Photo 11 and Photo 14 . They turn off at an angle of between 30° and 33° north of East, whereas the angles of the rows at Le Menec East are between 25° and 27° north of East. The four most southerly red lines on the bottom right of Figure 9 seem to converge to a point as do certain stones on the rows in the upper centre which show a change of direction. Only one line of stones, in yellow, aligns correctly between the central and eastern sections, but it links row 7 to row 8. The fact that there is a large section without any menhirs at all sheds doubt on any continuous system.

Figure 9 : Professor Thom's plan of the eastern section of the Le Menec rows. The red and yellow lines follow the actual stones.

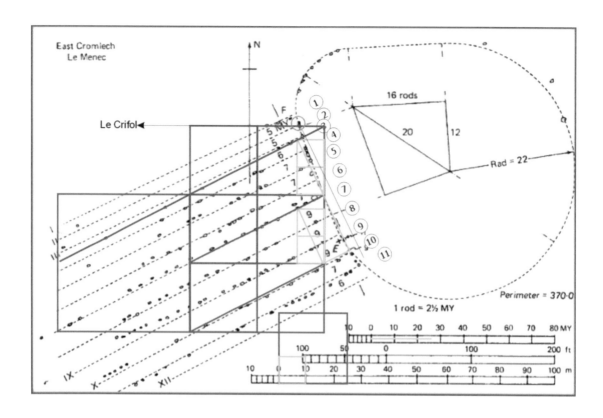

Figure 10: Double squares exactly position the rows at le Menec East. (plan and cromlech geometry by Thom.)

Photo 15 : Two touching stones at the start of row 2. Together they clearly suggest the right angle and the diagonal seen in Photo 8. The stone on the left is one and a half times wider than the one on the right, a 2:3 ratio, and its upper edge is the diagonal of a 2:3 rectangle.

Le Menec – Eastern alignments

Thom detected 12 rows in the East Menec section although it is difficult to count more than 9. There is only one stone on his row 1 and there does not appear to be any placed exactly on row 2. We shall nevertheless maintain his notation system, for the sake of clarity. The southern lines are much more accurate. The line on Thom's plan which goes through the most stones is row 9, even though it turns north after a certain distance. This could well be linked to the lie of the land as there is a natural crater here. He gives an angle for this row of 26.55° north of East (Table 3). This is the exact angle of the diagonal of a double square and gives us a clue to the general plan. I shall also suggest a replacement geometry of the cromlech since, in Thom's theory, the right hand side is not marked by stones.

Figure 10 shows how the organisation of the rows follows the same principles as at Le Menec West and how, once again, an incredible relationship is established between the metre and the megalithic yard, this time using the double square and its diagonal with the ratio of the square root of 5. If we consider row 3 to be the first row and we count the distance between rows 3 to 7 we obtain 27my (6+7+7+7). The space between the next three rows, 7 to 10, also adds up to 27my (9+9+9). This procedure is identical to the one shown for the western section, the sum of the width of the first four rows being equal to that of the next three. As the angle of the rows is that of the diagonal of a double square, the 27my measurement is shown as the diagonal of the green double square in Figure 10. The line between rows 3 and 7, when extended, runs exactly through the stones in the southern part of the cromlech. The left hand side of the green double squares, which are aligned North-South, precisely positions the western limit of the cromlech. They measure (see Appendix 2) 27 times 2 divided by $\sqrt5$ which equals 24.15my. When converted to metres, this gives 20.02m and shows that the single green square has sides 10m in length.

If the 27my length is now taken to be the **side** of a double square, from rows 7 to 10 for example, the diagonal of this new double square is 27 times root 5 divided by 2 which is 30.187my or 25.025 metres. This is now equal to the sides of the red square. We see how this positions exactly rows 2, 7 and 10. The diagonal of the uppermost red double square positions row 3 and goes through the stones in this row much more accurately than Thom's line. The diagonals of the next two double squares align perfectly on rows 7 and 10. These lines position the stones in the cromlech.

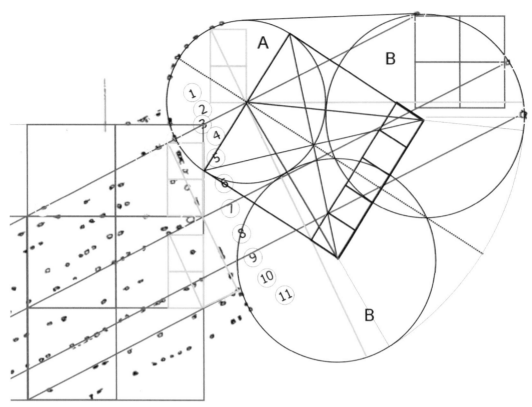

Figure 11: New geometry of Le Menec East cromlech (drawn over Thom's survey).

Photo 16: The two most easterly stones in the Le Menec East cromlech.

Le Menec East Cromlech

When rows 3, 7 and 9 are extended, they meet the 3 most easterly stones (Photo 16) in the cromlech (Figure 11). It is interesting to note that the upper two of these stones are on the corners of a half red square. These are very solid flat based blocks which are very unlikely to have moved since their implantation. I have consequently replaced Thom's type 2 egg with a different geometrical construction which, in my opinion, coincides with the actual positions of the stones, circled in yellow.

It is formed by 3 circles, two of which are the same size. Circle A, on the top left, positions the stones from the beginning of row 3 towards the north. Its centre is on the extension of row 3 and its radius is 27my, the green diagonal. Touching the right side of this is circle B1 which goes through the 3 stones mentioned above. The circle B2 touches the lower part of A at the extension of row 7. It goes through the stones between the start of rows 10 and 11 and overlaps the other circle B. This creates an axis which goes from the centre of circle A through the intersection of the two circles B and which is the same as the one on Thom's diagram. From the centre of the A circle, a curve can be traced which joins the two B circles together towards the south east. As the road runs through this section, there is, of course, no trace of it ever having existed. If, however, one end of a rope measuring 93.7476my or 77.7m (radius of circle A + diameter of circle B) is fixed to the centre of circle A and passed between pegs placed at the centre of the B circles, it would be possible to trace in one "stroke" the perimeter from the start of row 11 to the stone at the top of circle B1.

The centres of the two B circles are at the corners of the black square, perpendicular to this axis, which goes through the centre of circle A and **whose side length is 54my**, the diameter of circle A. This means that the purple lines between the centre of circle A and the centre of the circles B, Figure 11, are each the diagonal of a double square, 27my by 54my. This diagonal consequently measures 60.3738my which is 50.05m. This is exactly two red squares. The radius of the B circle is 33.3738my. Now 54 divided by 33.3738 equals 1.618033988... number known as the golden ratio or φ and which has the following remarkable properties.

$$1/\varphi \ + \ 1 = \varphi = \varphi^2 - 1$$

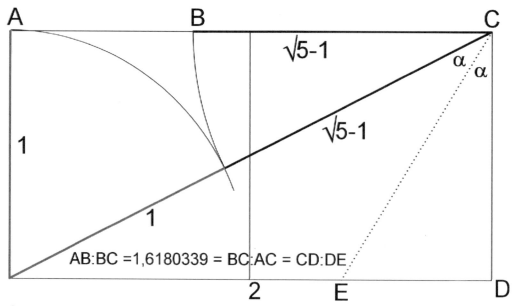

Figure 12: The golden ratio derived from the double square.

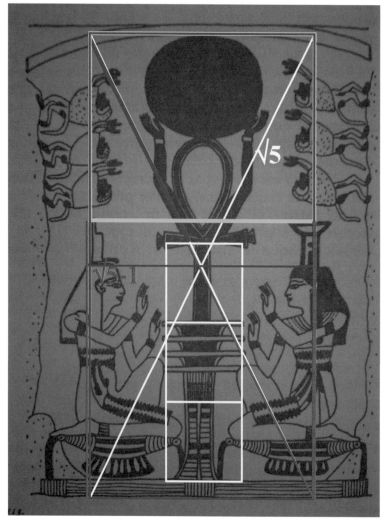

Figure 13:

An Egyptian painting organised using the double square (in blue) and the golden ratio. The two kneeling figures wear head dresses which mark the difference between the square and the golden ratio (in red). The height and width of the djed, the central column, is determined by the triple square. Its arms trace the diagonals of the double square.

It is derived from the double square (Figure 12) as it can be defined as follows:

$$\varphi = \frac{BC}{AB} = \frac{(\sqrt{5}-1)}{2-(\sqrt{5}-1)} = \frac{\sqrt{5}+1}{2} = 1.618033988...$$

It can also be derived from the Fibonacci series where a number is equal to the sum of the two previous numbers in the series.

1, 1, 2, 3, 5, 8, 13, 21, 34, 55, 89, 144, 233, 377 ...

When a number in this series is divided by a the preceding number the answer is an approximation of φ which becomes more and more precise, the further you go in the series. This proportion is to be found frequently in art from ancient Egypt and an example is shown in Figure 13.

The fact that 54my is equal to 44.76m with a value for the megalithic yard of 0.829m is worth pointing out here, since $2 \times \sqrt{5} = 4.472$. So we discover that the radius of circle A could well be $20 \times \sqrt{5}$ metres which would be most appropriate to the suggested geometry. Moreover, a megalithic yard of 0.8282m would give the exact correlation between 54my and 44.72m. Converted into English feet, we obtain 2.7171ft which is the "least standard" value of the megalithic yard as given by John Neal.[11]

Finally, concerning the measurements involved, the overall width of the cromlech is the sum of the diameters of the two different circles. This is 54my + 66.7476my = 120.7476my = 100.099m and we shall shortly see the significance of this.

The begged question now concerns the orientation of this cromlech. The axis is precisely 32° south of east. To a fairly high precision, it bisects the greater angle of a double square which is 90°-26.565°=63.435°, and divided by 2 = 31.7175°. From the centre of circle A, one green line extends the diagonal of the green double square while another extends its base, going east. The axis of the cromlech can be seen to cut this angle in two. Now this angle, 31.7175°, has another interesting characteristic. Its tangent is equal to $1/\varphi$!

This is, yet again, an **exact** correlation. We discover another astonishing property of the double square ! However, a closer look at the diagram gives a much closer and more intriguing result. The intersection of the two B circles in Figure 11 defines one fifth of the black square, 10.8my. The green lines cut the black square at four fifths of its length, creating a triangle 2.5 units high by 4 units long. This is a 5 to 8 relationship and the angle of a

Figure 14 : (above) The exact double square positioning the Le Menec West and East alignments.

Figure 16 : (left) The sole remaining Crifol menhir (encircled).

Figure 15 : (below) Detail of the Le Menec East showing how stones fall on the East West line and the diagonal.

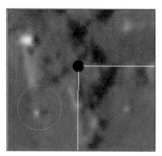

5:8 ratio triangle is 32.005°! So this result is given by the size of the intersection of the two B circles. 5 and 8 are two of the numbers in the Fibonnaci series and we are dealing with an incredibly beautiful geometrical representation of this mathematical expression, present in nature and the basis of growth. Once again, we see how the precise cardinal directions are the basis of the whole structure.

Le Menec – General plan

The diagonal of a double square orientated on the cardinal directions which goes from the beginning of row 3 at Le Menec East points to the beginning of row 11 at Le Menec West, and measures exactly 950m. I have verified this distance using a GPS device with 1cm precision.

Two touching stones, at the start of the supposed row 2 at Le Menec East, circled in blue in Figure 10 and seen in Photo 15, are of capital importance when looking at the global picture. Together, by their form, they suggest the right angle and a diagonal and are the exact counterparts of the two stones seen in the Le Menec West egg. Here they a have 2:3 ratio, showing the relationship between the double and the triple square.

The top right corner of the upper red double square, an extension of row 3 situated 11.18m (5 x root 5) inside the cromlech, is important in the overall geometry. A line drawn due West from this point, (Figure 15), goes through the two touching stones plus two others, supposedly in row 1. When extended, this line comes to the Crifol Menhir, Figure 16, sole survivor of a site mentioned by Gaillard and destroyed in 1905 by stone quarriers. The distance between the Crifol standing stone and the two touching stones is 860 metres. This menhir is also 430 metres due North of the start of row 11 at Le Menec West which is 961.18m (950 + 11.18) from the corner in the Le Menec East cromlech (Figure 14).

With extraordinary precision, we can see how the double square has been used on a very large scale. It should be obvious by now that all this work was done according to precise plans and with a definite intention. Before surmising what that may have been, we need to go further in our investigations.

Photo 17 : Stone rows at Le Menec East.

Photo 18 : The Tumulus Saint Michel seen from the North.

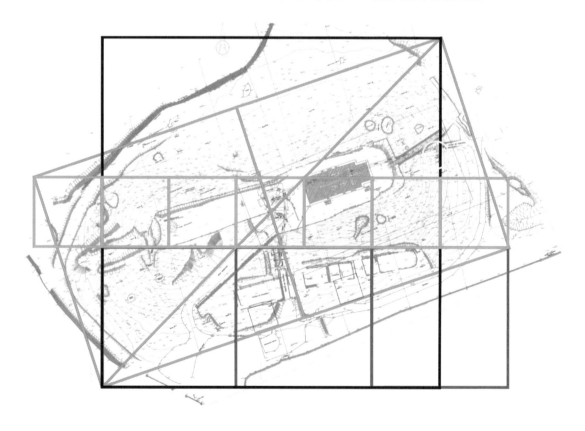

Figure 17 : 3+2=1 at the Tumulus Saint Michel.

Chapter 2 : Megalithic Landscaping

An incredible piece of prehistoric engineering, dominating the whole of the Carnac area, the Tumulus Saint Michel is an artificial mound weighing in at around 67000 tons. It crowns the summit of the highest natural hilltop in south Carnac and offers a 360° view to up to 40 km away. It was measured by René Galles in 1862 to be 115m long by 58m wide. It seems to have grown as its present dimensions are given as 125m by 60 m. We shall shortly see how this is possible. Excavations on the central and eastern part of the mound were very fruitful and many Neolithic polished ritual axe heads made from jadeite were found. This particular stone has been traced to a quarry in the Alps, around 1000 kilometres away. The official French government website is proud to announce that remains of human and animal bones were discovered in the heart of the monument along with Neolithic pottery. It then goes on to say:

"Attempts at radiocarbon dating from ancient samples have given results which are too diverse to be credible."

So apparently, despite all our fantastic dating methods and the abundance of archaeological evidence, we cannot believe what we find. This must suggest that some of the dates are far too old to be acceptable to the present model of prehistory. So archaeologists ignore them. Perhaps the discovery of the artificial mound at Gobekli Tepe dated at 9500BCE will enable our present model to evolve but I think it is our modern relationship with Time that urgently needs to be reconsidered. I personally do not believe one minute that the purpose of this monument can be explained by using the word "tomb" and I explained my reasons at length in my previous book. Here, we are simply going to consider its position and its geometrical organisation.

The starting point is given by René Galles' dimensions which are in a 1:2 ratio, suggesting the use of the double square. For many years, I pondered over the Tumulus' orientation which is N18.5°E, until I discovered the principle of the triple square. I then realised that the plan of the mound (Figure 17) was a double square (in green) aligned along the diagonal of a triple square (in red) which was orientated on the cardinal directions. As I was drawing the plan, the whole geometry appeared. The diagonal of the double square becomes the diagonal of a square (in black). This is an exact relationship, given here to three decimal places:

$$18.435° + 26.5655° = 45°$$

Photo 19 : The Tumulus Saint Michel seen from above.

21/06

21/03

Figure 18 : The side of the blue septuple square points towards sunrise at summer solstice

When we combine these two angles, we are in fact adding two irrational numbers (numbers whose decimals go on for ever) and obtaining a whole number. This is quite astounding and it led me to discover an entirely new approach towards ancient geometry and number. (see Appendix 3).

The width of the whole plan is 7 units (squares in blue), the triple square is 6 by 2 and the square has sides of 5 units. The square roots of 2, 5, 10 and 50 are contained in the diagonals of the square, the double square, the triple square and the septuple square respectively.

The diagonal of the black square is 5 x √2 (root 2) units.[a] (Figure 18).

The two central chambers are contained in the central blue square and the dolmen on the eastern side (in the yellow circle) is aligned to the side of the black square.

Four strange coincidences are worth mentioning.

Firstly, the path which leads up to the top of the mound runs along the diagonal of the square and the double square. When extended, this line is also the diagonal of the square cromlech at the start of the Kerlescan alignments, over 2 kilometres away, as we shall see later. It corresponds to the most northerly moonrise which happens every 18.6 years.

Secondly, the angle of the diagonal of a square, minus the angle of the diagonal of a septuple square gives the exact angle of a 3-4-5 triangle.

$$45° - 8.13° = 36.87°$$

In Figure 18, we see how the base of the blue septuple square which shares the same diagonal as the black square points towards summer solstice sunrise at the Carnac latitude. This line is also the diagonal of the red triple square which has been rotated to align to the axis of the monument. Its corner is marked by the stone staircase which is the other way to the top of the tumulus. The corner of the septuple square is positioned by a stone as seen in Photo 20. When this solstice axis is extended, it runs along the rows of stones at Le Petit Menec and positions the end of the Carnac alignments.

Could it be possible that these present day accesses to the summit follow the same directions as the initial design ?

The other diagonal of the red triple square is east-west and so points to sunrise at equinox. This is the same organisation as that seen at Le Menec West egg.

---

[a]It is the same as the diagonal of the green double square as √5 x √10 = √5 x √5 x √2 = 5 x √2 and also the blue septuple square since √50 = √(25x2) = 5 x √2

Photo 20 : A stone which positions the corner of the septuple square and shows the solstice axis along the staircase.

Thirdly, it can be seen that the present day chapel, built on the site of a ruined church in the 1920's, is perfectly positioned by the blue squares. In Figure 17, its diagonal is accurately placed along the top of the fifth square from the left and in Figure 18, its southern corners touch the sides of the inclined septuple square.

Finally, the small black squares show how the lines drawn by the surveyor on his plan are perfectly parallel to the sides of the double and triple square.

Of course, the urgent question which remains concerns the dimensions of this mound which could obviously be a key to understanding the Carnac site in general. As I have a 1:100 scale copy of the survey, very precise measurements are possible. However, the exact limits of the tumulus are not clearly defined. One must be wary of the recent dry stone walling which was positioned according to aesthetic considerations. The diagram presented in Figure 17 and Figure 18 gives very interesting results. The unit represented by the blue square measures 19m and the red square is its double, 38m. The triple square is then 3 times this distance in length, 3x38=114m which is very close to the size given by René Galles in 1862, and would fit if he had positioned the eastern end of the mound at the foot of the stairs. The observant reader will already have realised that the numbers involved here are *exactly* the same as those seen at Le Menec. The difference is the unit of measure, the megalithic yard being used at Le Menec West and the metre at Le Menec East and here. This metrological relationship between Le Menec East and the Tumulus Saint Michel is confirmed by their geographical connection on the same meridian, as we shall see shortly.

If the size of the tumulus is determined, as I suggest, by the double square, it makes it slightly longer, by a ratio of $\sqrt{10}/3$, which would equal 120.16m for the length and 60.08m for the breadth. This is 12 by 6 of the green squares seen at Le Menec East in Figure 11. The blue square, which determines the unit, has sides measuring 19m. The side of the black square measures 5 of these units making 95m and when multiplied by $\sqrt{2}$, we obtain its diagonal of 134.35m. This is extremely numerically close to a distance presented in my previous work, 1344m, which is the basis of a grid system using the 3-4-5 triangle and positioning the major monuments in the South Morbihan area of Brittany.

It must be remembered that all this becomes apparent because of exact orientation with respect to the cardinal directions. And this will be confirmed as we discover the relationship between the Tumulus Saint Michel and Le Menec West and East.

Figure 19 : The geometrical relationship between the Tumulus Saint Michel, Le Menec West and East and Kermario

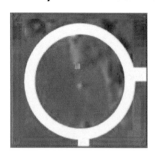

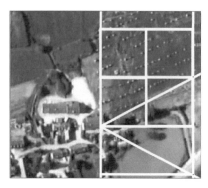

Figure 20 : (left) The last Crifol menhir is exactly in the NW corner , 4½ squares north of Le Menec West row 11

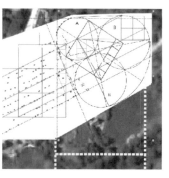

(right) The stones of the Le Menec East cromlech fit exactly into the 95m yellow dotted square, nine squares directly north of the central chamber of Tumulus St. Michel.

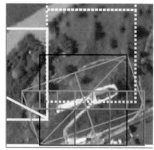

The Tumulus Saint Michel, Le Menec West and East relationship.

The double square relationship shown in Figure 14 between the two ends of Le Menec can now be refined and extended to include the Tumulus Saint Michel (Figure 19 and Figure 20).

The 95m black square found there, reproduced in yellow for more clarity, has been used to form a 9 by 9 square measuring 855 metres. The surviving Crifol menhir is exactly in the north west corner, the two touching stones at Le Menec East are in the north east corner and the west end of the central axis of the Tumulus Saint Michel is in the south east corner. The central point of the west side is the start of row 11 at Le Menec West. From this point, the theoretical diagonal to the opposite corner measures 855 m x √5/2 which is 955.92m and this corresponds accurately to the GPS data.

The Le Menec East cromlech and the Tumulus Saint Michel are included in this organisation by adding a tenth square to the east (dotted yellow). These two monuments are "out of line" by the same distance, the cromlech being offset to the north and the tumulus to the south. The most easterly stone in the cromlech falls to the right hand side of the square but the next stone up is aligned. When the uppermost square is adjusted to the top of the cromlech, the bottom of the ninth square down is exactly on the centre of the tumulus. If the bottom square is positioned at the base of the tumulus, the top square goes through the junction of the black square with the axis and the base of circle A, 54my south of the top stones, which, as we have seen, is 44.76m.

By adding 44.76m to 855m we obtain 899.76m as the north-south distance encompassing the cromlech and the tumulus. To understand where this "add-on" comes from, we must return to the Tumulus Saint Michel.

A further examination of the monument reveals the presence of half buried stones which surround the base. If we now extend our initial double square to include these stones with the "solstice stone" seen in Photo 20, a new structure appears, shown in Figure 21.

The central axis of the green double square is marked at each end by two recumbent stones and it positions the entrance to the chamber. When extended, this axis cuts the base line at a point T. From this point, two other lines may be drawn to other stones, circled in yellow, which lie along the northern side. One line, in yellow, is due North. The other goes to the corner of the black square. The size of the unit given by the blue squares now becomes 20m and the size of the black square, 5 units, becomes 100m. The red triple square is 6 units long, or 120m and its diagonal, which delivers the length of the tumulus, is $120 \times \sqrt{10}/3 = 126.49m$ which is now

Figure 21: The geometry extended to the surrounding stones (circled in yellow) at the tumulus Saint Michel

Figure 22: The double square and triple square relationship between Le Menec West and East, the Kermario dolmen and the Tumulus Saint Michel

very close to the "official" length. The distance from the bottom left hand corner of the black square, point O to point T is half this distance, 63.25m multiplied again by √10/3. This is equal to 60 x 10/9 which is 66.67m or two thirds of the black square.

This new geometry reveals an astonishing relationship, (Figure 22), between the Le Menec West, W, and East, E, the Crifol menhirs, C, the Tumulus Saint Michel, T, and the dolmen at the start of the Kermario rows, K. The geometry seen in Photo 15 on two touching stones is now to be found on a much larger scale. A rectangle composed of 6 yellow squares, 2 squares high by three squares wide, positions the Kermario dolmen, the Tumulus Saint Michel, the start of row 11 at Le Menec West and the top and centre of the Le Menec east egg. This shows the combination of the double and triple square and quite clearly shows how the Le Menec alignments were laid out and linked to Kermario. The precision is quite astounding on this scale with perfect orientation on the cardinal directions. The distances in metres between these different points, given by the satellite software, are reproduced in the following table.

	C = crifol menhir	E= East cromlech	K= Kermario dolmen	W= west cromlech	T= Tumulus St. Michel
C		900m	1350m	450m	1272m
E	900m		450m	1007m	900m
K	1350m	450m		1423m	1007m
W	450m	1007m	1423m		1007m
T	1272m	900m	1007m	1007m	

Three identical double squares each measuring 450m by 900m, two horizontal and one vertical, combine to make a 3 by 2 rectangle, like the one shown in Photo 15. The incredible precision of this structure is confirmed by the length of the diagonals, KT, WT and WE which all measure 1007m. Their theoretical length would be 450 x √5 which is 1006.23. Although recent constructions now block the view between Le Menec West and the Tumulus Saint Michel, a photo taken by Félix Gaillard in 1892 shows how the landscape was initially a plain on which the different monuments were implanted. The tumulus can be seen on the horizon behind a menhir on the far left.

In Photo 19, we can see the visibility between the Crifol menhir and the Tumulus Saint Michel, line CT, and also Le Menec West, line CW. CT is the diagonal of a 900m square and the distance of 1272m corresponds exactly

Photo 21: The Crifol Menhir with the Tumulus Saint Michel on the left horizon and the Le Menec West rows on the right.

Photo 22: The beginning of the alignments at Le Menec West in 1892(Félix Gaillard). The Tumulus St. Michel is in the yellow circle.

to the theoretical measurement. Finally, line WK, the diagonal of a triple square 450m by 1350m joining Le Menec West to the Kermario dolmen, is shown to measure 1423m which is precisely 450 x √10. It traces the first row of stones in the Le Menec West alignments and gives their direction.

Nine 100m black squares seen in Figure 21 join the base of the tumulus to the north of the Le Menec East cromlech which now fits precisely into the square (Figure 23). If we then trace another 9 squares to the west of the central square on this axis, we come to the western side of the Le Menec West cromlech. The top of these squares go through the Table Stone.

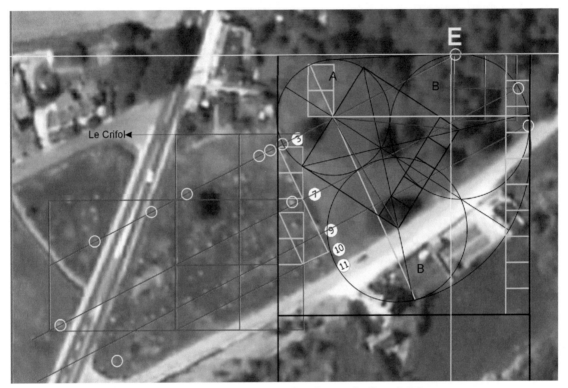

Figure 23: The Le Menec East cromlech and the 100m square

At Le Menec East, the column of green 10m squares is aligned on the west side of the black square and 10 of these can be seen to fit into it perfectly. The diagonal coming from Le Menec West runs along row 3, through the centre of circle A, and up to a standing stone, point E, which also marks the North-South axis. This stone is on the East-West line running from the Kermario dolmen to Crifol.

Before going deeper into the relationship between the Le Menec rows and those at Kermario, Figure 24 is an interesting summary of the geometry to be found at Le Menec. The two major directions of the lines are given by a septuple square. The western section runs along its sides while the diagonal positions the orientation of the eastern rows.

Figure 24: The blue septuple square at Le Menec. Its long side gives the direction of the Le Menec West rows and its diagonal traces the lines at Le Menec East.

Photo 23 : The Kermario dolmen with the beginning of the alignments.

It is placed exactly between the two cromlechs and its diagonal, as we have seen, measures precisely 950m. This gives the blue square a side length of 950 / √50 = 134.350288m. This is exactly the same length as the diagonal of the blue septuple square seen at the Tumulus Saint Michel in Figure 18, which was calculated as 7 x 19m = 133m then multiplied by √50/7 = 134.350288m. Consequently, if this septuple square is placed perpendicularly to the rows at Le Menec West, Figure 24, its diagonal traces the side of another septuple square which will mark precisely the stones in the cromlech at Le Menec East. A solitary standing stone circled in yellow at the top of the first blue square on the left could well be a remaining marker of this geometry.

We have seen that this method of arithmetical tracing gives exact angular results. The angle of the septuple square, extremely close to 8.13° is central to understanding. Here at Le Menec we see how the diagonal of the triple square plus the septuple square gives the double square.

$$18.435° + 8.13° = 26.565°$$

The angle of the septuple square, when doubled, gives the angle of the 7-24-25 triangle, seen to have been the basis of the Le Menec West cromlech.

$$8.13° \times 2 = 16.26°$$

A principle now emerges showing how, by doubling the angle of an arithmetical module with an odd number of squares, we obtain the corresponding Pythagoras triangle.

		Diagonal angle			Pythagorean triangle
Triple square	:	18.435°	x2 =	36.87° :	3-4-5
Quintuple square	:	11.3099	x2 =	22.62° :	5-12-13
Septuple square	:	8.1301°	x2 =	16.26° :	7-24-25
Nine square	:	6.3402°	x2 =	12.68° :	9-40-41

This series is infinite. I have learnt this fact by studying monuments which are 7000 years old. I do not remember having learnt this at school. It is in fact just the beginning of the understanding of an ancient language, whose aim was to express universal truth through number, when mankind spoke with one tongue, in the days before Babel.

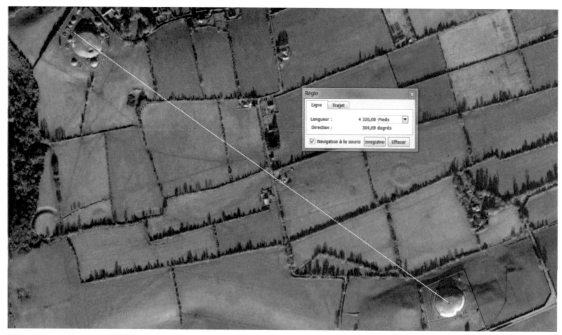

Figure 25: Angle and distance between Newgrange and Knowth.

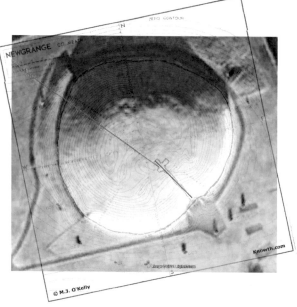

Figure 26: Knowth (above) and Newgrange (right) : Satellite view with plan superimposed. The Newgrange plan by O'Kelly was turned by 12° to coincide with the North on the satellite image. This also gives a correct angle for the winter solstice sunrise.

48

The monuments of the Boyne Valley, Ireland.

I have not been able to resist the temptation of inserting into the English version of this book a preliminary study of the monuments of the Boyne Valley in Ireland as their implantation corresponds exactly to the geometry we have just seen in Carnac.

The angle between the centres of two of these enormous neolithic mounds, from Knowth to Newgrange is E 34.69°S. This can be seen in Figure 25 and it is known to correspond at this latitude to the minor south moonrise which occurs every 18.61 years.

However, it also corresponds exactly to the angle of the diagonal of a septuple square added to the diagonal of a double square.

$$8.130° + 26.565° = 34.695°$$

This angle also corresponds to the diagonal of a 9 by 13 rectangle. These facts enabled me to establish the following plan (Figure 27).

Figure 27: Double square and septuple square relationship between Newgrange, Knowth and henge N.

It can be seen that the bottom centre of a third circular monument (henge N) is perfectly positioned at the bottom left hand corner of the double square. It has the same dimensions as the Knowth and Newgrange mounds and these three monuments all give the size of the square modules used to trace the plan.

Figure 28: Angle and distance between Newgrange and Dowth.

Figure 29: Geometry and metrology of Newgrange, Knowth and Dowth.

One can see in Figure 26 how the East and West sides of the Knowth mound have been straightened to indicate the exact dimensions of the square. In Figure 27, from the centre of Newgrange to the base of henge N we find a distance of 2 squares to the North and 14 squares to the West, the septuple square. The mauve line shows the angle of a 3-4-5 triangle, 12 squares at its base by 9 square high.

The distance given in Figure 25 between the centre of Newgrange and the N-W corner of Dowth is 4320 feet. This is a very important measurement which, as we shall see later, was used in Carnac. It is a canonical number, being 6^3 x 2 x 10 or 3x4x5x6x12. As it is along the diagonal of a double square, we must divide by $\sqrt{5}$ to obtain the side length. This gives 1931.96ft. This again is the diagonal of a septuple square and must be divided by $\sqrt{50}$ to give the size of our square module. The result is 273.2208 feet or 83.277m, which corresponds to the "official" size of the Knowth and Newgrange mounds. It is however a very special number as 27.3216 is the exact number of days in one lunar orbit.

The lunar aspect of Knowth is also enhanced by the presence of 127 kerb stones around its base. 127 is a major prime number (2^7-1) and as such is a mirror of the fundamental prime number, One. But it is also half of 254 which is the number of lunar orbits in the 19 year Metonic cycle which also counts 235 full moons. The exact relationship between the metre length and the foot is also to be found through this number, since 1 inch = 2.54cm. Also, a right angled triangle with a hypotenuse of 254m and a base of 235m has a third side measuring 100.0037 x $\sqrt{10}$ feet.

If we now turn our attention towards Dowth, we can see in Figure 28 that the angle between the centre of Newgrange and the North East corner of the mound is N58.28°E which gives E31.72°N. We recognise this as the axis of the Le Menec East cromlech, the tangent of which gives the Golden Ratio. This relationship can be seen in dark blue in Figure 29. The measurement is 6480ft which is precisely 1.5 times the distance between Newgrange and Knowth. By calculation, we obtain a distance of 1680.12m on the E-W axis, which is the measurement I have shown to be the basis of the meridian grid in the South Morbihan system. It is also a canonical number, expressed in metres here, as 1680 = 24 x 7 x 10.

It is also possible to calculate the exact distance between the N-W corner of Knowth and the N-E corner of Dowth. The result is 2777.77m which is 25000/9m or 25 x 111.11m or incredibly exactly 1.5 nautical miles! On the N-S axis, the distance between the two monuments is 288.88m or 2600/9m or 26 x 11.11m.

All the details of these measurements and calculations are given in Table 3.

I would like to point out here an interesting fact concerning the other major moon cycle which measures its phases. The average time between to full moons is 29.53059 days. To obtain the number of hours we multiply by 24.

29.53059 x 24 = 708.73416 hours

Now 708.73416 x 0.1111 x 127 = 10000.02.

This is certainly a very strange coincidence !

Finally, I would like to point out that the Great Circle which surrounds the Newgrange mound and of which 12 stones remain, has a diameter of 103.6m. This is 50 megalithic rods and again is a measure used in Brittany in the Kermario alignments, as we shall see now.

Figure 30: Continuity of the orientation of the stone lines from the start at Le Menec West to Kermario. Every other line has been traced to avoid overcrowding the image.

Figure 31: Close up of the beginning of the Le Menec West lines (below) and Kermario (right). These are extensions of the exact lines traced by Professor Thom.

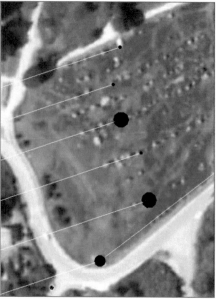

Photo 24: (right) Stones remaining from row 5 between Le Menec West and Kermario.

Chapter 3 : Three parts of a whole

Le Menec –Kermario

The beginning of the Kermario rows seems to be curved (Photo 2). Professor Thom suggested this and gave a radius of 1000mr. Despite his extremely accurate plans, I feel his interpretation is a close approximation which does not exactly follow the stones. My method has been to trace lines through **all** the stones and to examine the results. My conclusion is that the Kermario stone rows are a succession of straight lines which slightly change direction at certain points according to the principles of what has been called arithmetical or modular architecture.[12] The very start is in fact a prolongation of the beginning of Le Menec lines and so corresponds to the diagonal of a triple square, at an angle of 18.435° north of east. As we have seen, the most southerly row at Le Menec West runs towards the Kermario dolmen. It is clear from Figure 30 and Figure 31 that all the rows at Le Menec West link up to those at the beginning of Kermario. To my knowledge, this simple fact has never been pointed out. The stones at Le Menec East have probably confused the issue. Recent satellite software is an incredible booster to this kind of study.

I have traced every other line to avoid overcrowding the image. Figure 30 shows how most of the lines run south of Le Menec East although some go through part of it. In Photo 24 we can see two menhirs which are in the field north of the road from Le Menec to Kermario, just before we come to the junction at Le Menec East. In the top left corner of this photograph is the base of a house which at this junction. The stones are orientated 18.5° north of east and are in line with several other recumbent stones. They could clearly be the remains of row 6, the central line at Le Menec West, shown between the third and fourth yellow line from the north in Figure 30, which would have linked Le Menec West to Kermario, where it goes through the centre of the table stone and then continues much further to a distant foresight, as we shall see shortly. At Kermario, the most northerly line, row 1, continues the furthest before changing direction. This distance diminishes progressively in the rows to the south and at the dolmen, the change of direction is immediate. I have included the line marking the new orientation which goes exactly through the stones in the most southerly row and then runs to the very end, precisely to a menhir called Le Manio 2 which is by far the tallest stone at the eastern end of these rows.

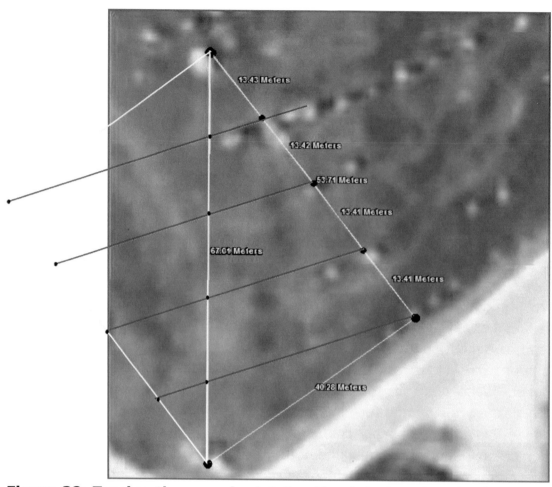

Figure 32: Tracing the rows by joining the dots in a 3-4-5 triangle.

Kermario (above) and Le Menec West (below)

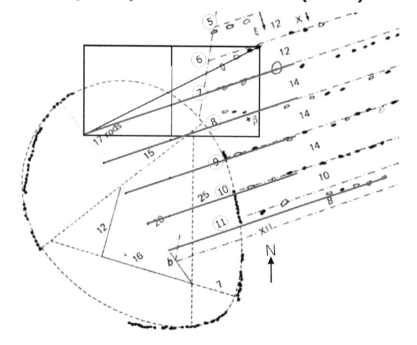

The first stone in this most southerly line corresponds to row 10 at Le Menec and the dolmen is in row 11. This new orientation of row 10 is 36.87° north of east, twice the initial angle and corresponding to the 3-4-5 triangle. As already pointed out, this aims at the sun's first rays as it rises at summer solstice, around the 21st June and also, in the other direction, towards sunset at winter solstice (Photo 28).

The 3-4-5 triangle was quite obviously used at Kermario many thousands of years ago to trace the beginning of the stone rows and their relationship with the dolmen[13]. The 5 side of the triangle was placed on a north-south axis, (Figure 32), positioning the centre of the Table Stone (Photo 29) and the entrance to the dolmen's chamber. The 4 side then marked the beginning of the 4 most southerly rows of the alignments and the 3 side gave the direction of the bottom row. The precise measurements can be seen with a distance of 13.43m as the basic unit, one tenth of the side length of the massive blue septuple square containing the Le Menec lines. We obtain the measurement of the N-S side as 67.15m, exactly 81my, the 4 side as 53.72m or 64.8my and the 3 side as 40.29m.

The same geometrical construction using the 3-4-5 triangle may well have been used to orientate the beginning of the lines at Le Menec West and Kermario. We have seen from Professor Thom's geometry of the Le Menec West egg that this triangle was also used there with its 5 side positioned on the N-S axis. Now, by joining up the dots which divide the 4 and 5 side into units we obtain lines which have exactly the same angle as a triple square, 18.435°.

The geometry for this is shown in Appendix 5. This implies equal spacing between the rows as is the case at the southern part of Kermario. It is also true for rows 7 to 10 at Le Menec West and could explain why 5 menhirs in row 11 are further south than those at the beginning (see Figure 32). The positioning and size of this new 3-4-5 triangle at Le Menec West gives yet another explanation of the monument's structure. When it is placed on the egg's axis and dimensioned according to the rows spacing, we find that the right angle, the extension of row 7, is precisely one unit from the egg's summit. From this same corner, the first four stones of row 6, inexplicably out of line, are now perfectly placed on the diagonal of a double square which is itself exactly twice the width of the triangle. These elements clearly seem to confirm its existence.

As the distance between the rows is 14my, the triangle's unit is $14 \times \sqrt{10}/3$ which is 14.757my. The width of the triangle, which is also the side length of the square, is 14.757my x 9/5 which equals 26.563my. The angle of the

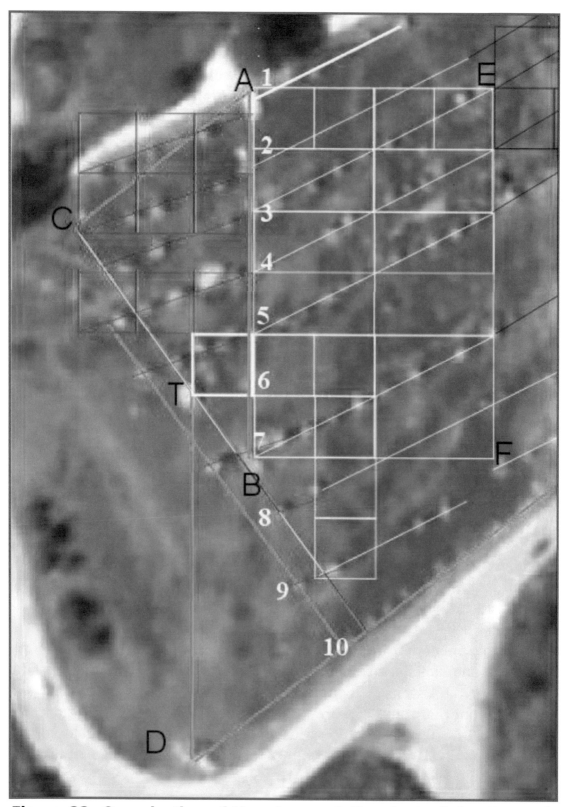

Figure 33: Organisation of the stones at the start of the Kermario alignments using the triple square (in red), the double square (in yellow) and the 3-4-5 triangle (in blue).

diagonal of a double square is 26.565°. Can this be a coincidence? If not, the builders had established a virtually perfect numerical and geometrical relationship between the side length of a double square and the angle of its diagonal expressed in degrees, the 360th part of a circle. If it is a coincidence, then I have just established this relationship. Also, 26.563my is equal to 22.02m, another very close megalithic yard to metre connection. It would appear very probable that the "joining the dots" method was used to trace the most southerly lines at Le Menec West and it is consequently not unlikely that the same method was used at Kermario. Here, rows 6 to 10 measure 64.8my compared to 64my at Le Menec West (12+14+14+14).

The Kermario Alignments

This same 3-4-5 triangle was then rotated through 180° (Figure 33) and the apex at point T was moved to point B positioning the corners A and C. Now the line AB measuring 81my was divided into six parts, shown by the yellow squares, giving a unit of 13.5my. Two of these yellow squares make a double square with a side length of 27my, the diagonal of the green double squares at Le Menec East and the diameter of circle A in the cromlech there. Thom gives a regular spacing between the northern rows with a distance of 12my. To obtain the N-S distance, we multiply by $\sqrt{5}/2$ which gives 13.42my, obviously very close to 13.5my obtained from deduction. From this new N-S axis AB, the rows of stones take the direction of the diagonals of the yellow double squares which perfectly position rows 1, 3, 4, 5, and 7. The start of row 2 on this axis, determined by the red triple squares on the left inside the triangle ABC, seems rather chaotic. Apart from the first stone just near point C, it is closer to row 3 than to row 1, which is not the case at Le Menec West. In this section, row 6 heads off in a different direction as will soon be demonstrated. Rows 7, 8, 9 and 10 start on the side of the 3-4-5 triangle as already seen.

The rectangle ABEF has sides with a 2 to 3 ratio. It is 4 squares wide by six squares high which is 54my by 81my. The rows trace the diagonal of a double square 54my by 27my which measures 50m, and then they change direction again, appently from the N-S axis EF. This axis is marked by a tall, wide and thin stone with a pointed top between rows 4 and 5 which Félix Gaillard called the index stone (Photo 25 and encircled in Photo 26).

However, Figure 34 using Thom's plans, shows how a line parallel to CB which also goes through the Index stone, this time along its axis, would seem to determine the the rows inflexion points. It appears probable to me

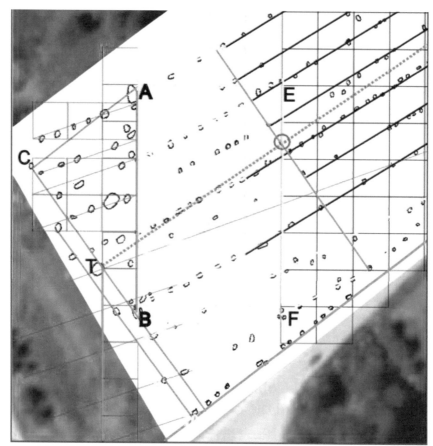

Figure 34: The index stone in the red circle indicates the point of inflexion.

Photo 25: The index stone between rows 4 and 5, perpendicular to the alignments,

that this line in conjunction with the line EF, creates a zone where the change in direction takes place, as many of the stones in this area are on the lines in both sections 2 and 3. In the following section the rows have a slope of 3 to 5 which gives an angle of 30.964° north of east. They extend between the axes EF and GH (Figure 35). The same module squares of 27my are used giving an E-W distance of 5 times 27my which equals 135my or 54mr (111.92m) and a N-S measurement of 3 times 27 my or 81my (67.15m). This can be seen clearly by following row 4 which is the third fine black line from the top. It starts precisely in the corner below point E and the cuts the top right hand corners of the smaller half module black squares and the double size 27my squares. These squares are on the same grid as the Table Stone and the dolmen.

Figure 35: The third section of the Kermario lines which follow a gradient of 3 by 5.

Photo 26: A close up of rows 2 to 5 showing the changes in direction and the index stone aligned with the Table Stone.

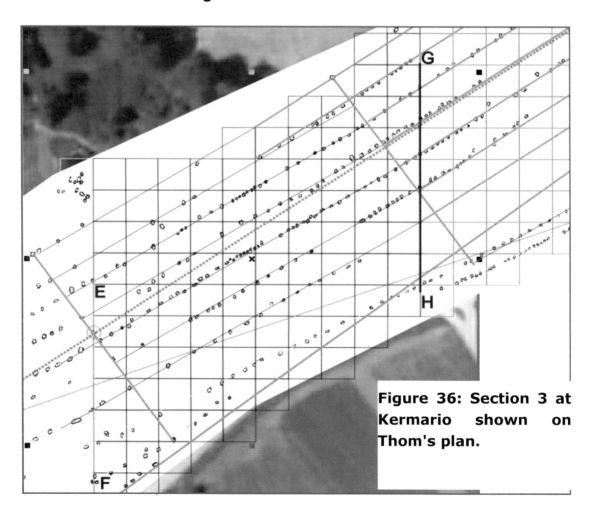

Figure 36: Section 3 at Kermario shown on Thom's plan.

Photo 27:

The Kermario Table Stone (right).

Photo 28:

Sunset at winter solstice along row 10 at Kermario (below).

The inflexion point would seem to follow the same principles as before (Figure 36). It is exactly the same geometry, superimposed over Thom's plan. A blue line parallel to CB cuts GH at row 6, marking also the change in direction in row 8. In the same way, a triangular zone is created which accommodates the change in direction.

In section 3, one can count 5 squares horizontally and 3 squares vertically. Row 1 has disappeared in the trees for the moment but rows 2 to 7 follow exactly this orientation. Row 6 reappears in this section, halfway between rows 5 and 7. We can also see the beginning of the fourth section but before examining this, we must look at what is happening in the southern part of the first four sections (Figure 37). Row 8 does not change direction at the EF axis but continues on the double square direction for

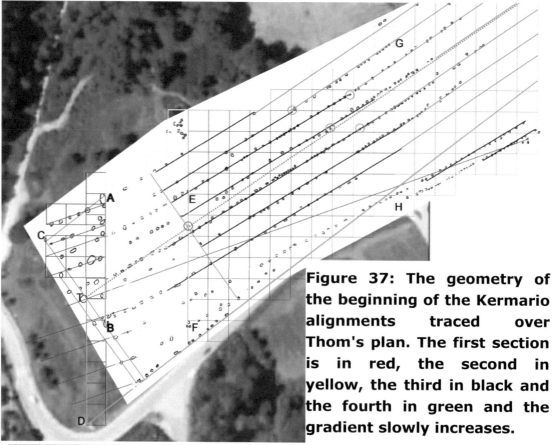

Figure 37: The geometry of the beginning of the Kermario alignments traced over Thom's plan. The first section is in red, the second in yellow, the third in black and the fourth in green and the gradient slowly increases.

Photo 29: The Kermario foresight aims at the Table Stone for long range precision with Le Menec West.

another 11½ modules east before turning to the 3 by 5 gradient at the blue line. Another row appears close to it on the south and follows the same inflexion. The two rows lead to two 3.5m tall menhirs with a 1.7m stone between them, far taller than anything around them. They look very much like the foresight on a rifle. By examining Photo 29, it can be seen that a thin menhir in row 8 is exactly at the centre of the Kermario Table Stone when viewed through this foresight. This line is traced in red in Figure 37 and it is the exact extension of row 6 at Le Menec West.

Satellite photographs shown in Figure 38 show how the line perfectly follows row 6 at Le Menec West, going through two tall stones near the hedge just before Le Menec East, the two remaining stones in the field seen in Photo 24 and the corner of the house at the junction, then the exact centre of the Table Stone at Kermario before coming to the three foresight stones. The total distance is 1680m.

Figure 38: Sighting over 1680m between Le Menec West and Kermario

The stones continue, the line goes through the corner of the house at the junction

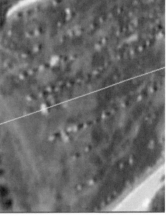

Start of row 6 at Le Menec West

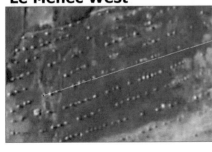

The line goes through the centre of the Table Stone at Kermario.

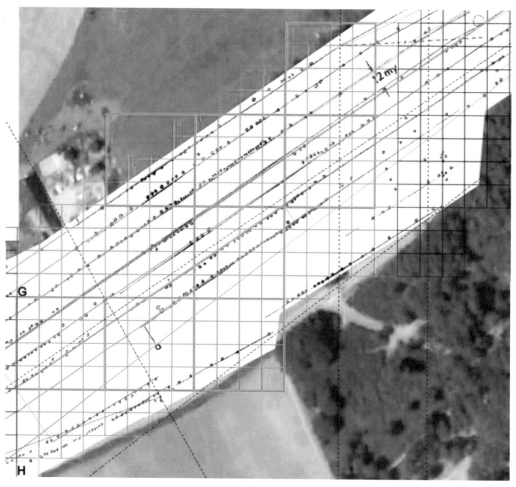

Figure 39: The alignments in section 4 at Kermario on a 2:3 slope .

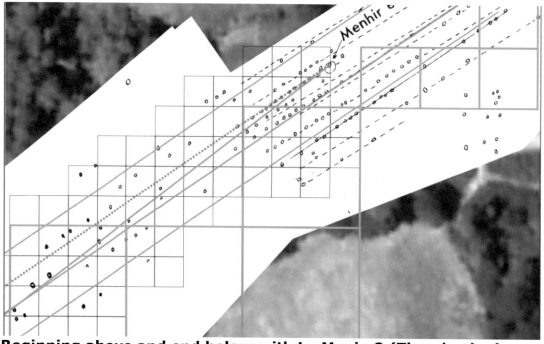

Beginning above and end below with Le Manio 2 (Thom's plan).

There is some kind of system in these southern rows which creates a stronger link with Le Menec West and the triple square orientation. The table stone is seen to play an important role.

Coming back to the northern Kermario rows, the fourth section is in green (figures 36, 37and 39) and the slope of the rows is given by the proportion of 4 squares wide by 6 squares high or a ratio of 2:3. This creates an angle of 33.69° north of east which is precisely half of the greater angle of a 5-12-13 triangle, well known as the second triangle of Pythagoras.

Row 1 reappears just after the farm, and all 7 rows follow the exact slope with correct spacing according to the grid. Professor Thom has marked the measurement of 12my on his plan and this can be checked between all the rows. The fourth section in fact extends right to the end of the Kermario alignments, despite a deviation between the two areas shown in Figure 39. Row 4 is shown here as a brown dotted line to distinguish it from the others because if it is extended from this section towards the south west it goes through the index stone and the centre of the Table Stone (figures 34, 36 and 37). Photo 26, taken from the top of the Kermaux Tower, a sort of folly near the centre where a dolmen once stood[14], shows the alignment between the Index stone and the Table Stone behind it. Extended towards the north east, row 4 brushes past the Kermaux Tower and runs up to the Manio 2 menhir, exactly 59 modules to the East of the axis GH. It links up here with the blue solstice line of the 3-4-5 triangle coming from the dolmen at the start of the Kermario rows, corresponding to the stones in row 10. This is extremely precise and will be shown to reveal also a standard of measurement.

The aim of the builders was to gradually increase the angle of the rows with respect to the E-W axis. They did this by starting with the triple square and then adding one square to the width and one to the height in each section. The same size module square was used in each section and the distance between the rows was determined according to this module. The sections were separated along N-S axes and the length of the sections increases from West to East. The slope and size of the lines is given in the following table:

	Section 1	Section 2	Section 3	Section 4
Slope	1 : 3	2 : 4	3 : 5	4 : 6
Width in modules	3	4	10	76.5?

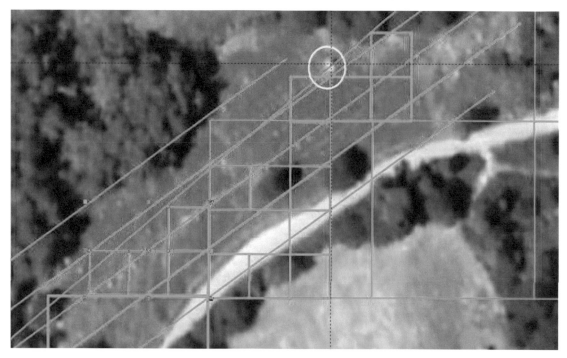

Figure 40: Satellite photograph at Kermario West at the end of the fourth section. The rows still follow exactly the same slope of a 2:3 ratio. Le Manio 2 menhir is circled in yellow.

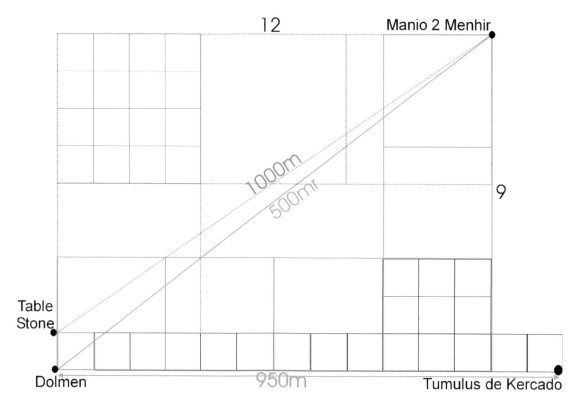

Figure 41: Kermario geometry with the Tumulus de Kercado.

The width of the final section is difficult to ascertain because its end is ruined. The distance given here extends to a final solitary menhir which we will discover shortly. However, this pattern is so clear that there can be no doubt about its being intentional and its scale has allowed it to survive for many thousands of years. Here we have a message which is coming, not from the depths of outer space, but from the long distant past... from before. Unlike the library in Alexandria, it has not been burned away.

An astounding global geometry now appears in this complex Kermario system (Figure 41). The major axis of the alignments is N56.31°E which gives an angle of 33.69° north of east. It can be measured exactly between the Table Stone and the Le Manio 2 menhir and corresponds to the stones in section 4. This is the precise angle of the diagonal of a 2 by 3 rectangle.

Between the entrance to the dolmen's chamber and Le Manio 2 is a line, marked by the most southerly row of stones and certain stones near the middle of the alignments, which is at an angle of N53.13°E or 36.87° north of east. This is the angle of a 3-4-5 triangle with the 4 side on the E-W line leading to the Tumulus de Kercado. The Table Stone and the dolmen are in a perfect N-S relationship, which I have verified using a theodolite.

The 2 by 3 rectangle and the 3-4-5 triangle consequently share the same E-W measurement. If we divide this side into 12 units, our 3-4-5 triangle becomes a 9-12-15 and our 2 by 3 rectangle an 8 by 12. So the rectangle has 8 units on the N-S axis and the triangle has 9. The distance between the Table Stone and the dolmen is thus 1 unit. So what are the measurements between these monuments? The Table Stone measures 3m by 4m. It has a large rounded bump in its north east corner which gives a

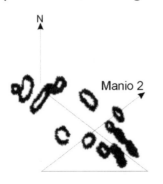

Figure 42: Thom's plan of the Kermario dolmen. The North, at the centre of the head stone, aims at the Table Stone position.

slightly higher viewpoint and this is the position I chose to place the theodolite (Photo 30). From here, the axis to the Manio 2 goes over the tip of the Index stone (Photo 31), and three stones in front of it, clearly out of line with the others in their row, show the direction. This point is due north of the centre of the dolmen's head stone, the vertical support stone in the centre of the northern wall of the chamber (Figure 42). The dolmen is composed of a corridor, directed towards sunrise at winter solstice, and a chamber. It was perhaps covered with a cairn of dry stone, making it higher and larger. The exact direction of the Le Manio 2 menhir , along the stones in row 10, cuts the dolmen between

Photo 30: Theodolite position on the Table Stone due North of the dolmen's headstone.

Photo 31: View N-E along the rows from the Table Stone. The Kermaux Tower can be seen in the distance, above the tip of the Index stone. The stones just in front of it indicate the direction (yellow line).

Photo 32: Le Manio 2 menhir seen from the side.

Photo 33: Theodolite views from the Table Stone.

Left: Dolmen head stone, N-S axis.   **Right: Kermario foresight.**

Photo 34: Stones in row 3 (centre) and row 1 (left), in section 4b, point to the Le Manio 2 menhir in the yellow circle , far in the distance.

the chamber and the corridor. So the exact geometrical corner is the junction point of the N-S axis and the solstice axis, which is also the tip of a 3-4-5 triangle with the dolmen on the hypotenuse. Due east of the dolmen, 950m away is the Tumulus de Kercado, at the triangle's right angle to the south of the original end of the alignments which today have disappeared. The exact direction of Le Manio 2. I have used a GPS device with a precision of 1cm to establish the measurements between the different points and have obtained the following results.

	Table Stone		Dolmen angle	
	m	my	m	my
Manio 2	1000	1206.27	1040	1254.52

These results are totally concordant with the theoretical dimensions given by the geometry. The diagonal of a 2 by 3 rectangle is $\sqrt{(2^2+3^2)} = \sqrt{13}$. So the theoretical distance between the dolmen and the Manio 2 is 15x1000/ ($\sqrt{13}$x4) which equals 1040.06. We can conclude that the geometry was implanted to perfection, using exact angles with respect to the precise cardinal directions.

Furthermore, the measurement of 1254.52my for the 5 side of the triangle is very close to 1250my or 500mr. In fact, if, instead of taking the measurement from the geometrical corner, we take it from the south side of the dolmen, we obtain 1036.8m. This gives the exact value of 500mr if we take the value of 2.0736m for the megalithic rod which is 0.8294m for the megalithic yard.

I quote Professor Thom:

"It appears that the megalithic rod was used in almost every line in the different sections (at Kermario). It seems that the builders were carrying their measurements over the inflexion points and were not using a new zero point at each elbow. An interesting point should be made here. We did our calculations supposing a unit of 2.073m and we found by measurement and statistical calculations that the observed intersections were advancing progressively as we went towards the north east. This can be explained if we suppose that the unit used by the builders was slightly longer than the one we were using."[15]

"This makes the megalithic yard 2.721 +/- 0.001 ft or 0.8293 +/- 0.0004 m which is comparable with the value found at the Kermario alignments."[16]

Photo 35: The ravine-filled lake which cuts through the rows. Le Manio 2 in a yellow circle.

Photo 36: Sunset looking uphill towards the Kermaux Tower, between the stones.

So our 3-4-5 triangle can also be seen as having sides of 300, 400 and 500 megalithic rods !

I must point out that Thom was making his measurements on the ground, whereas the GPS distances do not take the land's gradients into account, using horizontal values. This means that the builders were capable of measuring a horizontal kilometre over hilly land so they were not using paces! It also means that the global measurements will be different from the grid values. The basic global unit is 1040/15 = 69.33m which is 2.16m greater than the 67.15m basis used to determine the module and which enabled to precisely position the spacing between the alignments and the width of each section. 67.15m is the distance between the Table Stone and the dolmen itself, not the geometrical corner, so it is consequently shorter.

The measurement of 1036.8m as 500mr is also worth dwelling on, as 10368 is a canonical number, $12^3 \times 6$ and much used by John Michell in his ancient model of the world.[17]

Now, the stock of superlatives starts to run out and we are left in a state of wonder, mingled with bewilderment.

This extremely accurate measurement of 1000 metres on a 2 by 3 angle is obviously intentional, as is the 500mr on the 5 side of a 3-4-5 triangle. But who did it and why?

The Kermario alignments are not on a flat plain but, on the contrary, contain the most ups and downs in all the alignment systems. Photos 2 and 26 were taken from the Kermaux tower which marks the high point, approximately in at the centre. From there, going east, the rows go down a slope which becomes quite steep, into a ravine, which has been dammed to form a small lake, and then up the other side to another high point surmounted by the tall Le Manio 2 menhir (Photo 35). This stone, 3.5m tall, has a broad flat face which is perpendicular to the rows. It was clearly visible from the start of the alignments and then for their length from Kermaux (dolmen) onwards. In the section between Kerrmaux and the ravine, which we will call section 4b, the rows follow a complex detour which is another spectacular confirmation of the principles I have put forward.

I would like to stress the gratitude and admiration I feel for Professor Thom, without whose incredibly meticulous plans, none of these ideas could have emerged. The size of the monument, the lie of the land and the vegetation makes it impossible to get a correct idea of the detailed underlying structure by simply looking at the rows. However, as can be seen in Photo 34, the Le Manio 2 menhir was a guideline for implanting the stones.

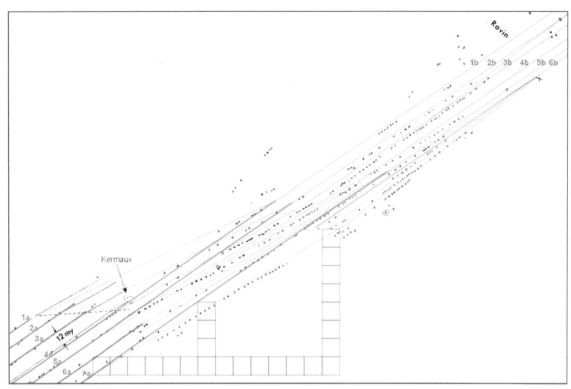

Figure 43: Section 4b of the Kermario alignments. The rows, marked by orange lines, convergent to the point X in the top right hand corner

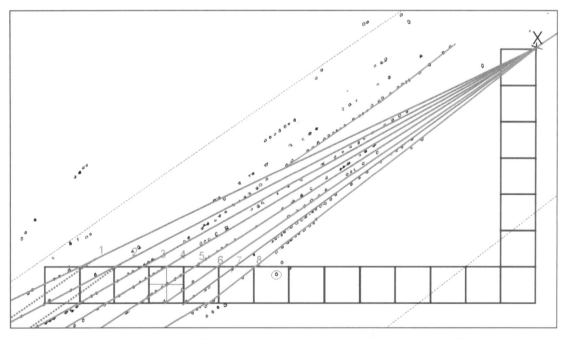

Figure 44: Arithmetical modules tracing the stone lines in the southern part of section 4b at Kermario.

Professor Thom suggests that the spacing between the rows narrows here to 10 my and then to $8^{1/2}$my. He apparently failed to notice that they are changing places (Figure 43). The seven northern rows in the first part of section 4, which we shall call section 4a, arrive at the Kermaux Tower at the top of the slope. As they come over the top, they start to converge to a point on their right, just on the other side of the ravine, marked on the plan by the point X (Photo 37). The stone lines do not continue straight on until they reach this convergence point, however. After a certain distance, they turn back to their initial 2:3 ratio angle, traced with thin green lines. The lines of convergence are traced by orange lines in Figure 43, although I have not traced the northern orange lines right up to point X to avoid overcrowding the plan. They stop at the point of inflexion.

Numbering the rows becomes difficult because they change places. I have decided to maintain the numbering of the rows from the North and I will follow the row number in section 4a by the small letter a and in section 4b by the small letter b. So row1a becomes row1b, in the continuation of the axis of row 4a, row2a disappears in section 4b but then reappears on the other side of the ravine, row3a becomes row 2b, in the continuation of the axis of row 5a, row 4a becomes row 3b, row 5a becomes row 4b, row 6a becomes row 5b, in the continuation of the axis of row 7a, and row 7a forks off to participate in a new fan of lines which appear to the south and which finish in a new line 6b. The rows 1b to 6b continue on the other side of the lake and run up the hill to le Manio 2. These new lines all converge to the point X and the most southerly, in blue, is aligned to summer solstice sunrise. The angles of all these lines correspond to the diagonals used in modular arithmetical architectural tracing, which means that the convergence point was chosen to allow this to be possible.

In Figure 43, we can see the angle of row 7a, after its first inflexion towards the south near the Kermaux Tower, shown by the purple squares, which is 4 high by 7 long or 29.74° north of east. This is the same as row 5a after inflexion.

Figure 44 shows how modular tracing was carried out in section 4b. Point X in the top right hand corner is the starting point of a grid 14 squares wide by 7 squares high. All 8 lines (numbered 1 to 8 starting from the left) converge to this point and certain lines go through the corner of a square in the bottom left hand side of the diagram. Lines 1, 2, 6 and 8 go through top corners and so one must count 6 modules for the height whereas lines 2, 3 and 7 go through bottom corners and are consequently 7 modules high.

Line 8 is shown in blue after it has turned northwards towards point X. The squares, 8 wide by 6 high, show that its angle corresponds to the 3-4-5

Photo 37: From the Kermaux Tower, looking East, the rows in section 4b converge to a point in the ravine before turning towards Le Manio 2. Taller stones under the trees on the right indicate the southern section.

Photo 38: Looking south west from Le Manio 2, the rows in section 4b turn as they come down the slope.

triangle. Line 7, in grey, is at a 7 high by 10 wide angle or 34.99° north of east. Line 6 is shown to be at a 6 high by 9 wide angle, which is 2 to 3, the general axis of section 4, and is consequently in green. These three rows all start with taller stones (Photo 37) on the same E-W line and their stones run along the convergence lines.

Line 1 is 13 squares wide by 6 squares high, 24.78°. Line 2 is 14 squares wide by 7 high, which is a double square, 26.565°. Line 3 is 13 squares wide by 7 high, 28.3°. Line 4 goes through the centre of the top of a square giving a ratio of 6 to $10^{1}/_{2}$ or 4 to 7, 29.74°. Line 5 crosses the centre of this square and so has a ratio of $6^{1}/_{2}$ to $10^{1}/_{2}$ or 13 to 21, a Fibonacci ratio, 31.76°.

In the top of the diagram, another blue line goes through stones which branch off from row 3b and which converge with row 1b at the Le Manio 2 menhir to the north east. This same blue line heads in the other direction towards Kermario row 10 and the dolmen. This shows that the solstice line was maintained for the whole length of the alignments.

The system of converging lines, seen in Figure 44, could very feasibly have a function as an observational calendar in the half season leading up to and coming after summer solstice, between what are known as the quarter days. Photo 37 shows how the sun would rise over a level horizon if there were no trees. The following table shows the dates corresponding to sunrise along the different lines in the neolithic period.

Line N°	Slope	Angle (E-W)	Increase	Date before	Date after	Days from solstice
1	6:13	24.78°		5th May	7th August	45
2	1:2	26.56°	1.78°	9th May	3rd August	41
3	7:13	28.30°	1.74°	13th May	30th July	38
4	4:7	29.74°	1.44°	17th May	26th July	34
5	13:21	31.76°	2.02°	23rd May	20th July	29
6	2:3	33.69°	1.93°	29th May	14th July	23
7	7:10	34.99°	1.30°	3rd June	8th July	18
8	3:4	36.87°	1.88°	21st June	21st June	0

We can see how, in the last 18 days, the sunrise moves only 1.88° on the horizon. For this period, dating by direct observation of sunrises needs a more sophisticated approach.

Photo 39: (above)

The Le Manio 2 menhir and rows crossing the low mound.

Photo 40: (left) A row of stones at Le Manio 2 aims at the Kermaux Tower, where there was once a dolmen, on a 2:3 angle.

Le Manio 2

On the other side of the ravine, the Le Manio 2 menhir (Photo 32), which is implanted in a low mound, was excavated by Zacharie Le Rouzic with M. and S.-J. Péquart in 1922. It has five serpents engraved at its base, a symbol which was found on two other upright stones there. Planted vertically in the earth in front of each serpent, Le Rouzic found five polished ritual axe heads made from fibrolite . This combination of serpents and axe heads may also de found engraved on the base of stone N°8 in the corridor of the chambered cairn of Gavrinis in the Gulf of Morbihan. The Association Archéoligique Kergal[18] has suggested at Le Manio 2 the existence of an engraved Sun positioned to the left of the serpents (Photo 41).

Photo 41: The Sun (in the yellow circle) and serpents on the base of Le Manio 2 menhir.

This representation, which was below ground level, has been preserved for many thousands of years. These undulating forms, rising from the ground are understandably very often associated with Earth energies and it will be shown later that the alignments are linked to the terrain's geological substructure. This is why the lines are sometimes not perfectly straight but wind around a central axis. The presence of the Sun, however, whose rays are straight lines, opens other horizons, indicating a relationship between the Heavens and the Earth.

The mound was built according to a complex plan and contains many small stone structures whose purpose is unknown. It was obviously a place of ritual for many years and there are the remains of hearths. It shows the existence of another aspect of the megalithic culture, far from our modern day understanding. The present alignments which run over it were re-erected after the excavations in 1923 (Photo 39).

The rows of stones do not stop at the Le Manio 2 mound and menhir but continue for some distance. Beyond the modern fencing which closes the site to the general public, the vegetation is extremely dense, but many stones may be found in it, some still standing (Figure 45). At least one line still continues through a wood, but then we come to a ploughed field and

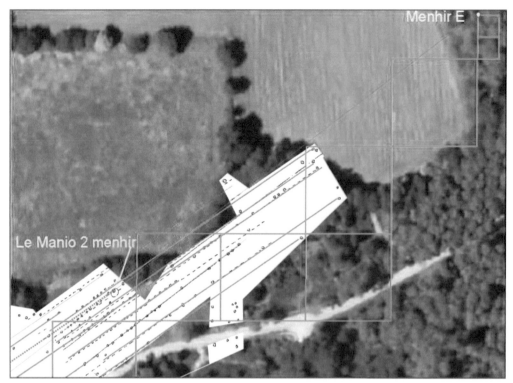

Figure 45: Menhir E on the solstice line from the dolmen.

Figure 46: Distances on the solstice line between the Le Manio 2 menhir, menhir E and Kerlescan.

Photo 42: Menhir E in the woods.

any stones which may have been there have long disappeared. However, on the other side of the field in another piece of woodland on higher land, a magnificent 2m monolith (Photo 42) is still standing. Thom called it menhir E. It is 256m from the Le Manio 2 menhir on the solstice line which starts at the Kermario dolmen. We can see how the stones running up to Le Manio 2 are exactly placed along this line. It is at a different angle to the other rows which maintain the 2:3 ratio except for one row, 2 lines up from the south, which also follows the solstice angle. Menhir E is a link with the next series at Kerlescan because if we now extend the solstice line further towards the north east, it arrives exactly at the angle of the Kerlescan cromlech. 539m separate the Le Manio 2 menhir from the corner at Kerlescan.

This is exactly 260mr. So we discover that from the Kermario dolmen to the corner of the Kerlescan cromlech there is a distance of 760mr on the 5 side of a 3-4-5 triangle. The menhir E is 1296m (1040+256) from the dolmen, which when divided by 5 then multiplied by 4 gives the E-W component. The result is 1036.8m or 500mr, the precise distance between the dolmen and the Le Manio 2 menhir !

Menhir E has a broad flat face which is orientated N153°E. This is perpendicular to a line E27°N which, when drawn towards the S-W exactly coincides with row 1 at Le Menec East and extends to the beginning of row 11 at Le Menec West. The total distance is 2695m which is exactly 1300mr, five times 260mr, the distance between Le Manio 2 and Kerlescan.

There is quite obviously some ingenious geometry going on here.

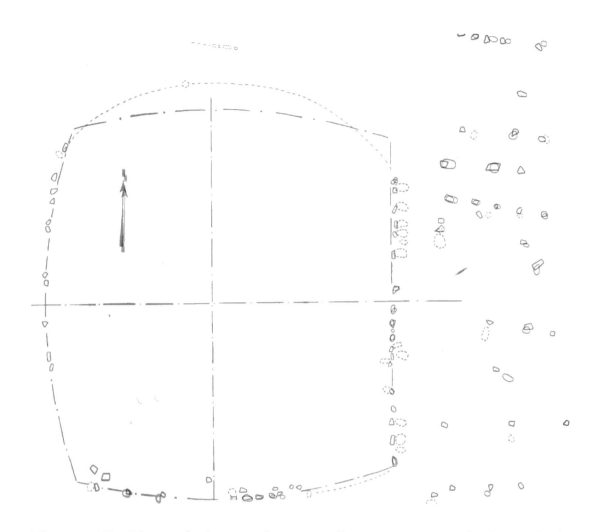

Figure 47: Plan of the Kerlescan alignments cromlech and the beginning of the rows. In grey is Lukis and Dryden's plan of 1870 and in red Thom's plan and geometry from 1972 so we can see which stones have been re-erected.

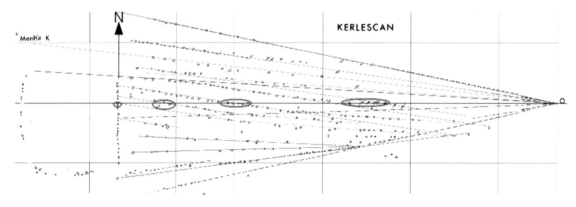

Figure 48: Kerlescan cromlech and alignments with lines of convergence.

Kerlescan

The megaliths at Kerlescan, like many others, have been subject to restoration work. There are many monuments here in different states of repair but the most well known are the alignments with a cromlech to the west. In Figure 47, I have superposed Thom's plan (in red) of the cromlech dating from 1972 to Lukis and Dryden's study done in 1870 (in grey). The cromlech lies on a plateau and is a perfect spot for astronomical observation although woodland now makes this difficult. The cromlech is square shaped with its west side curved. Lukis and Dryden did not record any stones on this side. It is most probable that they were incorporated into the bank which separated the plateau from the slope on the west. To the north, there are no stones but there are the remains of a long, low mound which apparently pre-dates the cromlech and is not visible on the plan. Several very low stones were used as an enclosure to this mound, but they are in no way part of the cromlech. Gaillard specifically states the absence of menhirs in 1884 and suggests that the cromlech had always been open to the north, as is the case at Le Menec West. Was it Thom's affinity to symmetry that made him draw a line on the northern side? The mound has a 3.5m tall menhir at its western end which is shown as Menhir K in Figure 48. 100m further north, the remains of another cromlech still exist. It must have been enormous and oval shaped originally but it is unfortunately now buried in woodland.

Many of the large stones on the East side of the plateau are now touching each other (photos 3 and 43) but 13 out of 20 stones have been re-erected. 5 stones at the centre of this line were still standing in 1870 and it can be seen that they are orientated along a perfect N-S axis. The other 2 stones which have always remained vertical are the first and the last which means that the most southerly stone which positions the solstice angle down to the Kermario dolmen has never moved. These two stones are not perfectly aligned N-S with the central ones. This has led many researchers to overlook the obvious N-S axis of the central section, which I have surveyed on two occasions with a theodolite and which is perfectly orientated and not deviated by 1 or 2 degrees, as often stated.

The southern side of the cromlech can be seen to have withstood the effects of millennia. All of its stones were still standing in 1870. Inside the cromlech, flat slabs of bedrock are visible (Photo 43). This is also the case at the start of the Le Menec West alignments and at Kermario, indicating a geological factor in positioning the sites.

Photo 43: Touching menhirs in their original N-S positions in the Kerlescan cromlech with visible bedrock in the foreground.

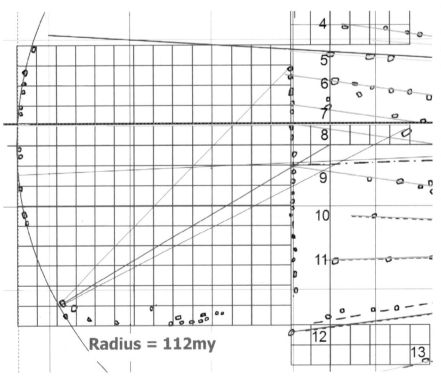

Radius = 112my

Figure 49:

The Kerlescan cromlech. The stones on the east side of the cromlech are on a N-S axis and are not deviated to the west by 1° as suggested by A. Thom. The 112my radius circle positions all the stones on the west side and its N-S diameter (in red) starts the rows.

The alignments go downhill eastwards from the plateau and here they are clearly converging to a point approximately 370m from the cromlech, 180 mr according to Thom, on the crest of the following hill. The point of convergence is situated in the village of Kerlescan, in someone's back garden on the hilltop, so this part of the monument has been destroyed, although there do seem to be some large stones in the ground there. Again, Professor Thom drew up very accurate plans to establish, none the less, its exact position which he called point O (Figure 48). In Thom's geometry, he drew a central axis (RO in Figure 48) which bisects the angle of lines and then decided that the cromlech was perpendicular to this and that it cut the cromlech into two equal parts. This led him to invent the line on the north side and miss the real geometry.

In fact, there is an E-W axis, perpendicular to the side of the cromlech, which is the basis for the rows' angles. From point O, the E-W line goes through many standing stones, (red oblongs in Figure 48), the first group being just south of the track. Further west, as it crosses row 6 , the stones change angle to run along it. Then it touches the north side of the Kerlescan index stone, a massive block of granite between rows 7 and 8, much bigger than the surrounding stones. When viewed from the west, it has a curved side on the top left (Photo 3 right of centre and Photo 44). The north side of another special stone in the cromlech, the sixth from the north, is also aligned on this same E-W line. It has a square summit, quite evidently because the top has been broken off, which means that it was most probably by far the tallest stone in the cromlech.

This axis is equidistant from the most northerly stone and the most southerly in the alignments, which are offset to the north with respect to the cromlech. The latter is cut into two unequal parts by the axis. The 14 by 14 square grid in Figure 49 shows that the cromlech's height and width are equal and that the E-W axis cuts it 4 squares from the top and 10 squares from the bottom. It is interesting to note that all the lines on this grid fall between the stones, on the east, south and west sides, frequently brushing past the side of a stone, and that very often, there are two stones inside a square. At equinox sunrise, on the 21st March and the 23rd September, an observer positioned on a mound near the west side of the cromlech sees the sunrise due east along the E-W axis and then, as the sun climbs into the sky, it rolls in a groove on the curved edge of the index stone for about 15 minutes until it "takes off" from the stone's summit (Photo 44). At sunset, an observation would have been possible from point O, this time rolling down the index stone into the ground.

Photo 44: Dawn at equinox. The sun starts its journey up the groove in the side of the index stone before flying from the summit.

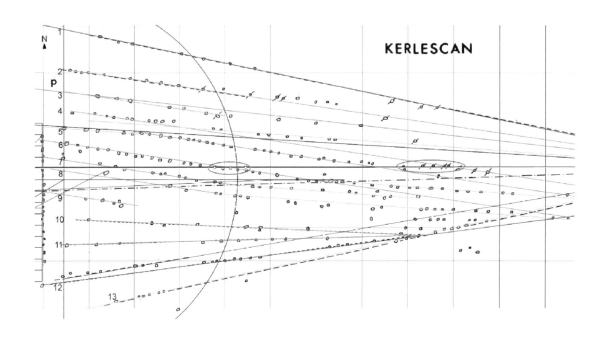

Figure 50: The different angles of the Kerlescan lines.

The stone in the corner on the bottom left of the cromlech is positioned perpendicularly to an exact 45° diagonal of a 12 by 12 square. In my previous book, I showed how this aims to the Tumulus Saint Michel and moon set at the most southerly standstill, every 18.61 years.

I have retraced the curve on the west side with a red circle that goes through **all** the stones, including the corner stone and the last stone in the bottom line both of whose flat faces are aligned on the curve. In Figure 51, there is another stone just to the lower right of the south-west corner stone, but I have seen no trace of its existence and it is not indicated on Gaillard's plan. The summit of the corner stone is curved, indicating a circle (Photo 45). Its radius is 112my, 16 squares of 7my. The centre of the red circle is at the centre of the beginning of the the alignments, between rows 8 and 9. Its N-S axis is marked by several large stones, the first in rows 2, 5, 6, 7, 11 and 12, and it is exactly 14my (2 squares) east of the cromlech. Its E-W axis is precisely one square down from the axis to point O and the beginning of row 8. From the centre of this circle to the south-west corner stone, the angle is given by the squares, 8 by 14 or a 4:7 ratio which gives an angle of W29.75°S. This, we shall see, is the principal angle of the lines at Le Petit Menec. The stone in the north-west corner is also slightly offset from the others and has a rounded, rather than flat, aspect. It is 5 squares north of the centre and 15 squares west, positioning it at the corner of a triple square, or W18.435°N.

The east side of the index stone is 6 squares east of the cromlech. This is 42my or 34.82m. So with respect to the stone in the S-W corner of the cromlech, it is positioned 9 squares north and 18 squares east, on the diagonal of a double square measuring 63my by 126my.

Thom suggested a radius of 60mr, 150my, for the curve on the west side which consequently missed a number of stones. This also obliged him to invent a corner in the south west and then two identical ones in the north west and north east, although not a single stone gave weight to this idea. I find this over simplification extremely surprising from an Oxford professor who, when speaking of the megalithic constructors, had said "*These people were more intelligent than I am*" and who had deciphered the extremely complex structure of the Avebury circle. I can only surmise that he had too little time when he came to Carnac and that the ruined state of the monument left things a little too open to conjecture[19]. His measurement of 150my would, however, be a close fit for the stones on the south side although there are other possibilities.

Figure 51: Convergence lines on a satellite photo

Figure 52: Convergence lines on an aerial photo. Index circled in black.

The precise angles of the first five rows from the north, which are all orientated towards the point of convergence, are shown in colour in figures 50 and 51 and explained in the following table.

Row	1	2	3	4	5
Colour	Red	Blue	Orange	Light Green	Mauve
Slope	1:5	1:7	1:9	1:13	1:17
Angle (E)	11.31°	8.13°	6.34°	4.40°	3.36°

This precise and progressive change in angle shows conclusively that modular architectural tracing was used to position these alignments and that the East-West axis is central to its organisation.

There is some confusion concerning row 5 which, on the satellite photo aims perfectly to point O whereas on Thom's plan, it deviates to the south, following the exact angle of rows 2, 6 and 7, in blue. One can see quite clearly in Photo 3 taken from the air that rows 5 and 6 are not at all parallel and that row 5 is pointing well to the left of the house, directly to the point of convergence. Also, two stones circled in yellow in Figure 52 are exactly on this line and the one nearest point O (photo) has its flat face aligned along it. Was there some confusion between rows 5 and 6 when the plans were drawn up?

Rows 6 to 9 start in blue and then change direction in light green, so they go from a 1:7 slope to a 1:14 slope, or half the gradient. Rows 6, 7 and 8 change direction on the circumference of the red circle. The rows turn again to an E-W direction. This means that the rows remain parallel. Row 6 turns on the axis which aims to point O.

To the south, unfortunately, the building of the road has destroyed part of the rows. Today, the final line, row 13, aims clearly at the point of convergence, as does the beginning of row 12. On the plan, it then seems to turn south to join rows 10 and 11 which together converge to a different point. This is exactly the same principle as in section 4b at Kermario where three lines converge onto one line which then continues further. In the aeriel photograph, however, (Figure 52), the stones in row 12 appear to continue in line towards the point O. Their angles are summarised in the following table.

Row	10	11	12(S)	12 (N)	13
Colour	Green	Green	Purple	Black	Yellow
Slope	1:21	1:42	1:8	1:6	3:14
Angle (E)	2.72°S	1.364°N	7.125°N	9.46°N	12.09°N

Photo 45: The south west corner stone at Kerlescan on the right. Its summit is clearly curved, showing it is part of a circle.

Photo 46: The west side of the cromlech with the north-west corner stone on the right.

Photo 47: The N-S axis on the East side of the Kerlescan cromlech. The top of the sixth stone from the left has been broken off. It was once the tallest menhir in the cromlech and marked the E-W axis.

Photo 48: Menhirs under the trees in row 1 at Kerlescan.

Photo 49: Kerlescan row 13 near the road

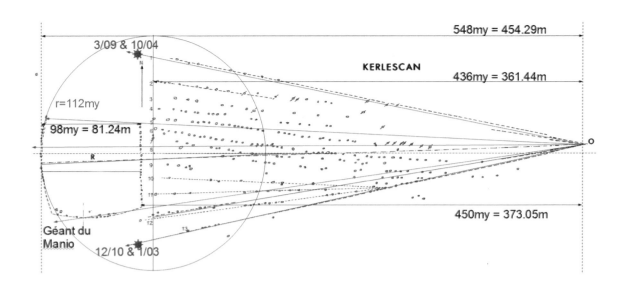

Figure 53: Measurements and calendar at Kerlescan. From observation point O, the lines indicate sunsets 20 days before and after equinoxes. The south side of the cromlech is aligned to the Le Manio giant and indicates a 10 day period. From point O to the East side of the cromlech is exactly 450my or 180mr. The cromlech is a square with a side length of 98my.

Photo 50: The groove in the Index stone at Kerlescan where the sun rolls up and down at equinox sunrise and sunset.

In conclusion, rows 1 to 5 and rows 12N and 13 aim directly at point O. Row 6 finally aims there along the E-W axis after changing direction twice. Rows 7, 8 and 9 run parallel to the south of row 6. Rows 10 to 12S converge to a stone on row 13. The fact that 8 rows converge on point O is totally conclusive of its existence. Two rows would have been enough to make a hypothesis. It must consequently be considered as being extremely important and should be the focus of some archaeological excavations, which have never been undertaken, if the present landowners have no objections.

If these converging lines are astronomical sight lines, (see Figure 53) the angles represent sunrises 20 days before and after equinox, from the 1st March to the 9th April at spring and from the 3rd September to the 12th October in autumn. Now, from autumn equinox on 23rd September to spring equinox on 21st March following there are 179 days whereas there are 186 days between spring and autumn equinox. We would explain this nowadays by saying that it is because the Earth's orbit is elliptical, not circular. For an observer, this means that the sunrises move slightly faster in winter than in summer and so are not perfectly symmetrical around the E-W axis. We have seen that this is also the case for the lines at Kerlescan. Row 1 is E11.31°S whereas row 13 is E12.09°N, a little more than half a degree different.

This would suggest that the observations were made towards the setting sun from point O, which is a much more practical solution than sunrise, as one has the time to anticipate where the sun will disappear. Now we can understand why only rows 1 to 5 and rows 11 and 12 converge to point O since they point to either side of the cromlech. From point O, the cromlech's southern corner is at a 1:9 slope or W6.34°S and its northern corner on a 1:17 slope or W3.36°N. So the sun sets into the cromlech for 15 days, 10 days to the south of the E-W axis and 5 days to the north, with an average shift of 0.646° per day, approximately its own size on the horizon. If the object is to anticipate equinox, then the sun enters the cromlech from the south, 10 days before spring equinox on March 11th. Now on this particular day, it would also set directly behind the biggest menhir in Carnac, Le Géant du Manio, on the hilltop 439m behind the south east corner stone, giving a high precision backsite.

15 days is length of the cycle between new moon and full moon. So when the full moon preceding spring equinox sets in the North-East of the cromlech (seen from point O) and the sunset that evening is aligned to the southern side and the Manio Giant, then 15 days later, at new moon, the sunset and moon set will set take place simultaneously in the North-East corner. These are moments when the combined gravitational effects of the

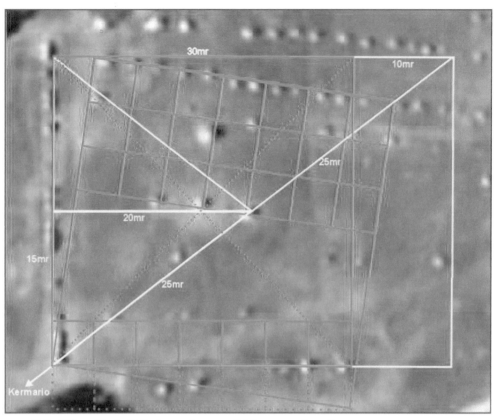

Figure 54: The 3-4-5 triangle and the septuple square.

Figure 55: 1680 metres between the Kermario dolmen and the Kerlescan 3-4-5.

sun and the moon are at their greatest, creating high tides.
The precise dimensions of this site are explained below (see Figure 53).

The overall length from the west side of the cromlech to the convergence point is 548my or 454.29m. The maximum width of the cromlech is 81.24m or 98my. This is 14 x 7 and confirms the grid in Figure 49. This means that the distance from point O to the east side of the cromlech is 548my - 98my= 450my or 180mr. In metres this is 454.29 – 81.24 = 373.05m. The alignments start 14my east of the cromlech, giving them a total distance of 450 – 14 = 436my which is 361.44m. The length of the stones in the N-S axis is 65.4m or 31.5mr and the diagonal measures 97.75m. If this is divided by $\sqrt{2}$, we get a theoretical value for the side of the square as 69.12m or 83.33my. 83.33my divided by 7my equals 11.9 squares, which is why the corner stone just cuts the corner of the twelfth square. 69.12m is equal to the unit found in the global Kermario calculations as 69.12m multiplied by 15 gives 1036.8m or 500mr.

We must take a closer look at the central section of the alignments at Kerlescan. South of the index stone, there are few stones but they are massive. The largest is on the extension of the solstice line linking with Kermario (Figure 54) and exactly at the centre of the N-S axis thus creating two 3-4-5 triangles with it (in yellow). Moreover, the dimensions of this triangle are 15mr x 20mr x 25mr, exactly the same size is the one used at Le Manio 1 site, as we shall see later. The yellow rectangle thus formed has a diameter of 50mr, so the total distance from its N-E corner to Kermario is 760mr + 50 mr = 810mr, which is 1680m, the same distance as the diagonal of the triple square from Le Menec West to Kermario (Figure 38).

Now row 6 has a 1:7 slope and we have seen on page 37 that when the angle of a septuple square is added to that of a 3-4-5 triangle, we obtain 45°, the diagonal of a square. These considerations lead to the geometry seen in Figure 54. A N-S orientated blue square with a side length of 30mr has a large stone exactly at its centre, as shown by the two blue dotted diagonals. The height of this square is determined by the first stone in row 6. Two other stones, which belong to row 12, in its bottom right hand corner show that the side length should be divided into 7 units. The beginning of row 11 can be seen to be positioned one unit from the base. This square has then been tilted to a 1:7 slope, as shown by the seven dotted squares added under the base. Its size has been slightly increased by the proportion of $\sqrt{50}/7$ to coincide with the diagonal of a septuple square. The top of this

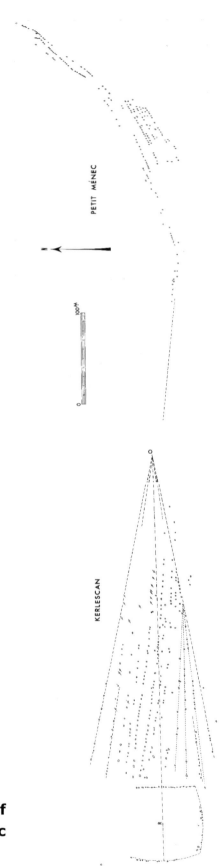

Figure 56: General plan of Kerlescan and Le Petit Menec (A. Thom)

slanted square is marked by a line of 13 stones, row 6, its diagonal by the solstice line from Kermario, and the centre of its base line by a menhir.

It can also be seen that when this square is divided into 7 parts, rows 7 and 9 are precisely positioned. The first and fifth stones in row7 are exactly on the sides of the square. The 3 large stones in row 9 are at the corners of 3 consecutive squares. Row 8 starts further to the east and does not seem to have been part of this structure.

The size of the diagonal of the slanted blue square is equal to its side length multiplied by $\sqrt{2}$ which is 30mr x $\sqrt{50/7}$ x $\sqrt{2}$ or 300/7mr. The unit of the straight square is 30mr/7 which means that the diagonal of the slanted square is 10 times the unit of the straight square. This process which replaces square roots and irrational numbers by simple geometry is an important part of the megalithic way of thinking. Again, the numbers 3 and 7 and the septuple square play an essential role in the conception of this magnificent work of Art.

Le Petit Menec

A calm shaded footpath between dry stone walls heads east from the village of Kerlescan, crosses the main road from Auray to La Trinité and leads us, just on the other side, to the alignments known as Le Petit Menec. No massive stones are to be found here. It is nothing like the start of Le Menec, Kermario or Kerlescan. Of course, the building of the road has seriously perturbed this section, but even so there can be very little doubt that this is not the beginning of a new series of alignments but the continuation of the Kerlescan site. These alignments are not closed to the public by fencing and offer an extremely pleasant and shaded visit on a hot summer afternoon. The other side of the coin is that, because of the vegetation, it is very difficult to get a global picture of the site. So, once again, we must turn turn to Professor Thom's invaluable plans to understand how these rows are organised. Certain details here give valuable insight as to the actual method used for tracing.

There are three major sections in this monument which correspond to three different orientations. The first few stones, on either side of the path after the road, are more or less E-W. We then come to Felix Gaillard's engraved stone (Photo 55), which tells us that Le Petit Menec is state property and after this, the first clear row of stones can be seen.

Figure 57:

Changing direction in section 1.

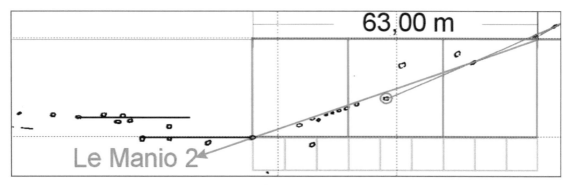

Figure 58: Le Petit Menec section 1.

Section 1

This row constitutes the first section and is on the angle of a triple square, whose long side measures 63m. Several large stones in the bank to the north suggest the existence of another row. It can be seen in Figure 58 that the module is again the 7m square, so this section, in green, is 9 modules long by 3 high. The row points precisely to the Le Manio 2 menhir, which is not however directly visible from here.

The stone in the mauve circle is an interesting example of how the change in direction was made between this section and the next (Figure 57). It is a very flat slab which has been orientated in the row's direction, which enables us to realise that it is part of the row, but has been placed slightly south of the row's axis.

This can be seen in the photo on the left, looking, south-west. The photo on the right shows how this stone is aligned to the next three stones in the row. This corresponds to the mauve line in Figure 58. The next stone is exactly on the initial green line but the following one is to the north of it and just south of the mauve line. This is the stone that marks the junction between the two sections and is in the top right hand corner of the green triple square. Finally, the next stone is well north of the green line but exactly on the mauve line, which serves an intermediary direction between sections 1 and 2.

We shall see more examples of this technique in the other sections.

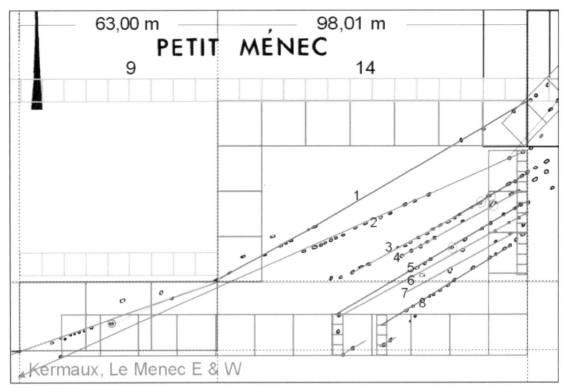

Figure 59: Le Petit Menec geometry of section 2.

Photo 51: (above) A junction stone seen from above. Its V shape enables it to align to two different orientations.

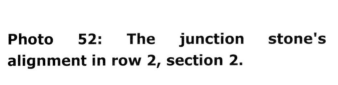

Photo 52: The junction stone's alignment in row 2, section 2.

Section 2

Two rows, which run for the whole length of section 2, converge on the junction stone. Row 1, the furthest to the north, is at first in orange on the same angle as four of the six most southerly rows, E28°N, a 9:17 slope. It then changes to brown on an 11:19 slope, E30.07°N. The overall angle of section 2 is consequently a 4:7 slope, E29.75°N, which can be seen by the large orange squares. This is very close to a Pythagorean triangle.

$$4^2 + 7^2 = 65 \text{ and } \sqrt{65} = 8.06$$

Row 2, in mauve, is at an angle between rows 1 and 3, which are far apart but it starts in fact at a stone near the beginning of section 1. This row is extremely important and will reveal an essential aspect of the Carnac alignments that we have not yet discussed. It is E22.62°N, which is the angle of what is known as the second triangle of Pythagoras, the 5-12-13. It measures 161.65m or 195my which is 15 x 13. So the unit of this 5-12-13 is 15my or 6mr. As the three sides add to 30 units, this makes a total of 180mr which we have seen to be the length of the Kerlescan alignments. This apparently insignificant row actually traces the general axis of the alignments from their beginning at Le Menec West.

The six rows to the south of this section can be seen to be positioned by the mauve squares. Rows 3, 4, 6 and 7 are orange while rows 5 and 8 are brown. Rows 5 and 6 converge to a stone at the corner of mauve square 7. Row 5 shows very precisely the angle of $4^3/_4$ by $2^3/_4$ mauve squares which resolves to 11:19 or 30.07° as mentioned.

So the rows are gradually turning north. First, the green 1:3 slope, then the mauve 5:12 and the orange 9:17 and finally the brown 11:19. All the lines except row 4 finish on a N-S axis, which gives us the width of this section, 14 modules of 7m which equals 98m. The last two stones in rows 3 and 4 are no longer on the initial axis and it is obvious that they have turned further north and are part of section 3. The first stones in row 3 are also out of line, on a lesser angle, which gives this row the overall appearance of a curve. We shall come back to this point.

I have drawn red circles around stones in rows 3, 4 and 5 as they are much taller than the surrounding stones. I believe that it is because they have a double function and are used for sighting over longer distances. A yellow line can be seen to go through two of these stones and also several others, and particularly two on the top right side in section 3.

Rows 1 and 2 of section 2 turn to follow an E45°N angle and again the junction stones are of great interest. When examining row 2, I realised that two stones in it were missing from Thom's plan and I have added them in

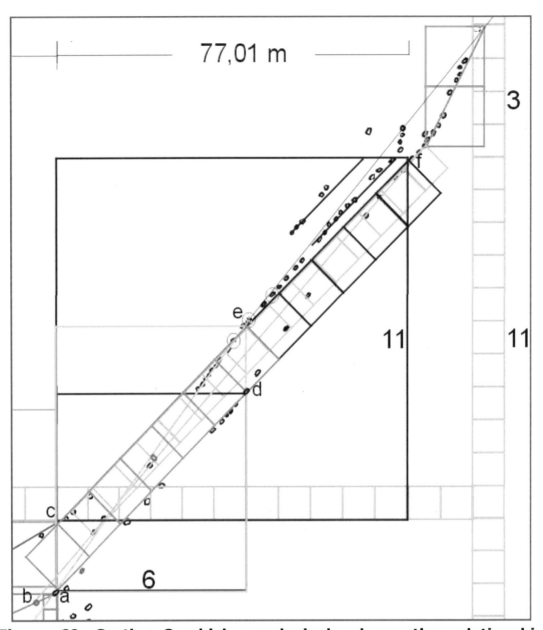

77,01 m

3

11

11

6

Figure 60: Section 3 which conclusively shows the relationship between the square, the 3-4-5 triangle and the septuple square.

Photo 53: The rows of stones at a 45° angle from North at the top of the slope in section 3.

red as they are essential. The one on the left is on the junction of a line in section 3 and the mauve line, row 2. Photos 51 and 52 show how the stone's V shape enables it to play a double function, being part of two lines. The missing stone added in red on the right is a flat stone whose face is orientated E45°N showing clearly that it is already part of section 3.

The junction stone in row 1 can be seen perfectly in Photo 54. In the foreground is the first, flat stone in section 3. Behind it, much taller, is the junction stone which is V shaped. Its left side is aligned with section 3 while its left side can be seen to be in line with the stones in the distance which are in section 2. We can also see how the wall changes direction at precisely this point. It was most probably built around (and with) stones in a row which has disappeared.

These different examples of how the rows change direction bring home the extremely well thought out nature of these monuments and make us realise that **each stone** is an ancient monument and must be preserved at all costs. There can be no first and second class stones, some that receive great attention whilst others are abandoned to non-specialised land owners. Our priorities need to be revised.

Section 3

Sections 1 and 2 go along the valley floor but Section 3 starts at the base of a slope and runs up to the top. Its geometry is organised around the diagonal of a square whose side length is equal to 11 khaki coloured modules of 7m making a total width of 77m (Figure 60). The diagonal measures 77m x $\sqrt{2}$ = 108.9m and goes from point c to stone f, which is right-angled with a diagonal side (Photo 58). The diagonal is also divided into 11 modules, in black and blue, whose side length is 7m x $\sqrt{2}$ = 9.9m. The two outer rows are separated by this distance.

Points a and c, the two junction points of rows 1 and 2 are on the N-S diagonal of an additional 12th module astride sections 2 and 3. Between point a and point e, the tallest stone at Le Petit Menec situated at the top of the slope, a row of stones cuts between the two outer rows (Photo 56). This line is the continuation of the yellow line already seen in section 2, which cuts across the lines there through the tallest stones. It is at the exact angle of a 3-4-5 triangle, N36.87°E, as can be seen by the yellow rectangle, 6 khaki modules wide by 8 high. But this line is also the diagonal of a blue septuple square of the 9.9m module. This is a perfectly clear example which conclusively shows the relationship between the square, the 3-4-5 triangle and the septuple square, orientated to the cardinal directions. Point d is the last

Photo 54: Junction stone in row 1.

Photo 55: Section 1 row 1

Photo 56: The stones change direction in section 3, row 1.

Photo 57: Heavily eroded flat-faced stone along the diagonal of the septuple square. Behind it is the square block at point d.

Photo 58: The small right-angled stone with a diagonal marks the corner of the square (point f). In the left foreground, the taller stone is again part of two rows.

Photo 59: Menhirs north of the road after the "end" of the alignments.

Figure 61: Distant extensions of the rows at Le Petit Menec.

stone on row 2. It is again on the N-S diagonal of the blue module square with respect to point e but also at the corner of a 6 khaki module square whose diagonal, a to d, is row 2. This square block can be seen in the background in Photo 57 and seems to be adequately shaped to fulfil its role. However, another, more subtle line needs to be examined. It goes from stone b to three stones after stone f and contains 12 stones. It is the diagonal of a 16 fold khaki square whose centre is at point e where it perfectly coincides with the blue square. It determines the width of the intermediate row near point c. This 16 fold square is consequently 112m long (16x7) and its diagonal is at an angle of 3.576° with respect to its side. As its side is already at an angle of 45°, this line is at 45°+3.576° = E48.576°N which is a slope of 17:15.

As we have already seen that the diagonal of a seven fold square added to the diagonal of a square gives a slope of 8:6, we have a pattern emerging here. The principle is that when the diagonal of an n-square is added to the diagonal of a square, the resulting slope is n+1/n-1. This can be verified in the following table.

n	2	3	4	5	6
angle	26.565°	18.435°	14.036°	11.31°	9.462°
+45°	71.565°	63.435°	59.036°	56.31°	54.962°
Slope	3:1	4:2	5:3	6:4	7:5

Were the megalithic builders pointing this out or were they simply using these principles to construct their work of Art ?

So in section 3, row 2 moves over to take the place of row 1. As another row appears to the north at the end of section 3, it is probable that row 1 moved over also but that the stones have disappeared.

At point f, the main row suddenly forks north at an abrupt angle (Photo 58). The line is too short to get an accurate direction but it is around N11°E, perhaps a 5:1 slope. The row to the south also deviates to the north, but to a much lesser degree, on approximately a 2:1 slope. This is represented by the blue double square in Figure 60. After a gap of 16m, 3 well aligned, squat stones, which were not on Thom's plan, show a lesser angle. Four fallen stones are nearby. They seem to be aiming at stone e, but the zone is too ruined to make any conclusions. We then arrive at the road which is the "official" end of the alignments. However, on the other side in the woods, the stones continue in thick undergrowth (Photo 59). This means there is a section 4 which is impossible to survey for the moment.

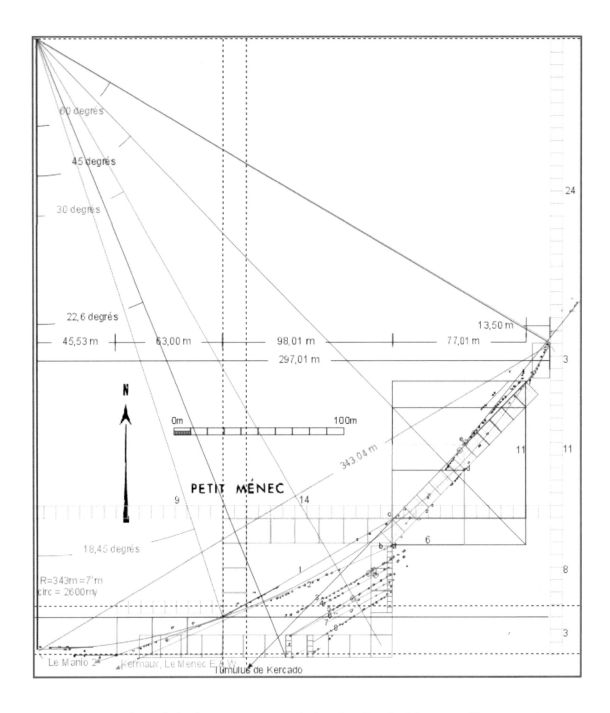

Figure 62: The global geometry of the Le Petit Menec alignments.

The Le Petit Menec circle

As the rows at Le Petit Menec are the final part of the Carnac alignments, it is most enlightening to see how they aim at all the major Carnac monuments (Figure 61). Row 1, section 1 (Photo 55), the triple square, is aligned to Le Manio 2. Row 2, sections 1 and 2, on the angle of a 5-12-13 triangle, goes right to the Table Stone at Le Menec West. It goes through a ruined cromlech south of Kerlescan, then along ruined alignments south of the road (Photo 60) to the point of convergence at Kermario section 4b, then through the Kermaux tower and the Le Menec East cromlech and rows. This obviously makes it the major axis of the Carnac alignments, as was suggested in 1983 by the Association Archéologique Kergal[20]. The Tumulus Saint Michel is at an exact solstice angle, 3-4-5, and section 3 extends at 45° to Kercado.

I mentioned earlier that the stones in row 3 section 2 closely resembled a curve and, of course, the continual process by which the alignments turn towards the north would suggest the curve as general outline to these rows. The result of this study is at the least spectacular and comes as an astounding confirmation of the proposed hypotheses. In Figure 62, I have traced a circle which gives the best fit to the real position of the stones and takes into account important points that we have already investigated. I should point out that all the measurements and angles shown in this diagram were generated by a computer program in French on the 1: 1000 scale plan I was working on. Consequently, they are not approximations or figures that could have been rounded up or down, but precise results.

One sixth part of the circle is shown here and it corresponds exactly to the length of the alignments. Its radius is 343m which is 7 cubed. When this is multiplied by 2 pi to obtain the circumference the result is 2155.13m. If, instead of pi, we use 22/7, which was always the ancient approximation as immortalised in the Great Pyramid at Gizeh, the result is 2156m which is equal to 22 x 49 since one factor of 7 disappears. This is also 11 x 98, numbers we have seen to have been used in the construction of the alignments. When this measurement of the circumference is converted into megalithic yards, we get 2600my which is 1040mr ! The distance in a straight line between the beginning and the end of Le Petit Menec is shown as 343.04m, showing an equilateral triangle with the centre.

It is now possible to understand what these megalithic people were doing and how they were operating. They were tracing a gigantic circle on the ground, and as they could not do it on this scale with a stretched rope, they

Photo 60: An unknown stone alignment in the woods on the line between Le Petit Menec and Le Menec

Photo 61: The Kerlescan Dolmen looking south-west.

worked with segments and tangents based on the cardinal directions and modular arithmetical geometry. So the first section, which uses the triple square, opens a segment of 18.44°, the angle of the diagonal of the triple square. This falls exactly on the junction point between sections 1 and 2 and the curve goes right through it, so row 1 is tangent to the circle at this point. Row 2 then takes over and is tangent to the circle at 22.6°. It can be seen that this radius, when extended, cuts precisely the base of the 7th square of the 5-12-13 triangle, the axis of departure for the southerly rows in section 2. The following radius, at 30° from the start, is perpendicular to these rows and coincides with the corner of the 5-12-13 triangle. Row 1, however, is not tangent to the circle here but is a chord.

The 45° angle can be seen to bisect the 11 module square starting at point a. The curve goes through the two upper corners of the 12 squares that form the diagonal and also through the stones to the south of the main row. From point f upwards, the stones are exactly on the circle. This monument is so precise, that despite 7000 years and some destruction, there can be little doubt about the builders' intentions and this serves as a clue to what the other alignments are about. We have already seen that the Le Menec and the Kermario lines behave in the same way, deviating towards the North, but before looking into this, it is very tempting to trace the entire circle at Le Petit Menec to see if it goes through any megalithic sites.

My first action, after having discovered the exact measurements, was to position the centre of the circle. This proved extremely difficult, despite very accurate equipment. It is in woodland which was cut down and replanted several years ago and the terrain is now practically impenetrable, being thick with young gorse approximately 2m high. As it is on private property, it is not possible to use a flame-thrower ! Also, someone has made the most of the areas inaccessibility in order to grow cannabis plants and so I was half expecting some customs officers to jump out from behind the bushes. When finally, covered in scratches and thorns, I located the central position with the GPS, there was a kind of soft mound, most probably made up of branches and leaves left behind by the lumberjacks. By climbing on this, I was could see that I was on the hilltop. Just south of me, the land went down steeply, which would have offered perfect visibility for the megalithic circle builders at Le Petit Menec. I was also able to mark a reference point on the GPS, which was useful later in pinpointing other parts of the circumference. If there is anything megalithic at the centre, it is well hidden. Local people here have a tendency to throw their trimmings over stones since the land is not useful for anything else and it stops nosy people

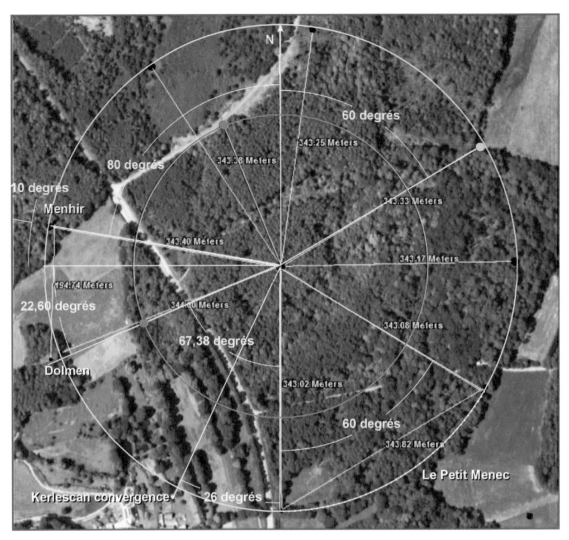

Figure 63: The full circle of the Le Petit Menec alignments.

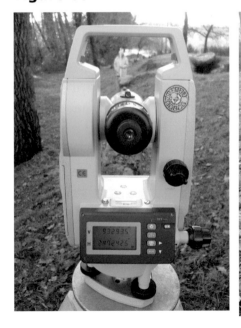

Photo 62:

Kerb stones on the south side of the Kerlescan dolmen mound point to the centre of the Le Petit Menec circle on the angle of a 5-12-13 triangle.

from hanging around on their property. I personally went to see the mayor of La Trinité sur Mer four years ago to complain about the fact that a classified and unique "double-decker" dolmen at Kervilor, several hundred metres south of the Le Petit Menec alignments, is under a massive heap of rotting vegetable matter which comes from the adjoining camp site. This site was excavated in 1864 by the Société Polymathique du Morbihan and then by Félix Gaillard in 1885. He discovered an unknown chamber **beneath** the main chamber, with many intact ritual objects. This is the only case of a two floored dolmen known to exist and it is still, in August 2010, hidden to the world under a huge compost heap. Then people ask why Carnac is not a World Heritage Site !

When one looks at the aerial photograph of the Le Petit Menec circle, (Figure 63), taken before the trees were cut down, it is astonishing to see how a circle is formed around the central point by a gap in the woodland ! Could it be that an inner circle of stones exists and has affected the vegetation? Upon inspection, many fallen stones are to be found in this area but a detailed survey is impossible under the present conditions.

Many interesting things are to be found on the circumference of the Le Petit Menec circle not the least of which is the Kerlescan dolmen (Photos 61 and 62). An accurate theodolite survey shows how the southern kerb of this monument points straight to the centre of the circle on the exact angle of a 5-12-13 triangle orientated on the cardinal directions. This means that the 13 side of the triangle equals the radius of the circle, 343m, which in megalithic yards is 413.6my. The unit is one thirteenth of this, 31.818my or 100 x 7/22my or 100 divided by pi. This is because the circumference, as we have seen, is 2600my, a multiple of 13.

One third of the way along this hypotenuse about 225m from the centre, again lost in thick undergrowth, one discovers what seems to be an unknown cairn, with some massive blocks of stone on and around it (Photo 63). An ancient pathway goes through the edge of it and the stones from the monument have been used at this spot to build the bordering dry stone walls. The eastern wall, however, is much higher than the western wall, showing how it cuts through the side of the mound. To the west of the path, on the edge of the field, several standing stones can still be seen. The ruined mound is shown in Figure 63 by a small orange disk placed on an inner orange circle, between the dolmen and the centre of the circle. The old track actually follows this orange circle north until it reaches the modern road, where it disappears. I would not have mentioned this ruined monument had it not been for the fact that another mound is to be found (Photo 64) at the same distance from the centre of the circle at exactly 90°

Photo 63:

Ruined megalithic site on the 5-12-13 hypotenuse.

Photo 64: Mound and stone circle near Le Petit Menec.

from it, so consequently 22.6° W of N. This small mound is also unknown although it it surrounded by a stone circle with six remaining stones. Coming back to the outer circle, shown by the Le Petit Menec alignments, a well know standing stone, around 3 metres high is to be found very close to the circumference (Photo 65), due north of the dolmen.

At the most northerly point of the circle, I could find no trace of any stone. However, when I continued following the circle towards the East, I came to the remains of yet another mound, shown by a small green disk in Figure 63, just near the corner of a field. This turns out to be exactly 60° E of N, the same arc as the alignments, so together, they slice the eastern half of the circumference into three. There is much study remaining to be done in this area, as there are many remnants of alignments transformed into walls and massive blocks of granite littering the woods, but this goes beyond the scope of the present work, whose aim is to show the underlying principles.

What we have discovered so far can now form a platform upon which we can construct a more global picture of the Carnac alignments and the other monuments surrounding them.'

.

Photo 65: Menhir on the Le Petit Menec circle.

Conclusion

This study has shown us that many thousands of years ago, thinking beings undertook the work of building a gigantic monument using the principles of modular architecture. In the main, they used the most elementary geometrical forms; the square, the double square, the triple square, the septuple square and the 3-4-5 triangle. This work shows the relationship between these different forms, which seems to have been forgotten since. This geometry was organised according to the cardinal directions with a very high level of accuracy. It has only recently become possible to verify this fact using sophisticated instruments such as high precision GPS, lasers and electronic theodolites.

Every series of alignments in Carnac turns towards the North, suggesting segments of circles. These circles traced by the builders get bigger and bigger the further we go east from Le Menec West, which seems to be the most southerly point in the Carnac alignment system.

We have seen how at Le Petit Menec part of the circle is traced by alignments whilst other kinds of monuments (isolated standing stones, earth mounds, dolmens...) are positioned on the circles circumference. It is important then to discover if this same principle was used on a greater scale, and this is exactly what I have done. However, as my research advanced, it quickly became clear that my findings went beyond the scope of this present work, where I had decided to concentrate on the Carnac alignments.

I have consequently decided to stop this present work here. It already provides food for thought. I shall continue this quest, unravelling the reasons for the Carnac alignments, in a second volume which I hope to finish shortly.

I am well aware that the conclusions presented here are difficult to believe, despite the consistent evidence. We must call into question everything we think we know about our prehistoric ancestors if we wish to approach this forgotten ancient intelligence. I have spent over twenty years living in the Carnac area and trying to come to terms with the implications involved. Although I am certain that much more could be discovered if a correct way of thinking evolved, having myself the permanent impression of "looking through a glass darkly", and despite certain negative reactions that I am sure will ensue, I have decided to try and share my findings.

Work in this domain has become much easier since the advent of computer programmes and Internet applications such as Google Earth and Skyline

Globe which provide high resolution satellite images and tracing tools. Time in the field remains essential however, as it allows a "contact" with the builders. Many technical problems and human difficulties had to be overcome to achieve this gigantic architectural masterpiece.

Here at Carnac, the scale is so gigantic that one cannot visually take in the whole picture. Modern construction, roads and tree growth are slowly erasing the original work of art. Our society is not aware of this catastrophe. These incredible remains from humanity's forgotten past are not a World Heritage site. They are not even classified by UNESCO. So building and development continue, making it more and more difficult to experience the whole picture.

The efforts undertaken at the neolithic period were not, however, in vain since, thousands of years later, the megaliths remain and they speak openly to all who wish to listen to their universal language, a language that is written in stone, in form and in number.

Acknowledgements

"No man is an island, entire of itself."
John Donne, (1572-1631)

I would like to give thanks for all the help I have received, be it visible or invisible, in the course of this study.

In the field, the members of the Association pour la Connaissance et l'Étude des Mégalithes (ACEM) and in particular Thierry Maho, the president and also Jean-Yves Colin and Françoise, my wife.

For the study, Professor Thom's plans were essential as was the work of the Association Archéologique Kergal and its founder, Madame Fleury, I could also mention Pythagoras, and more recently Jay Hambidge, Matila Ghyka and Georges Jouven,

Special thanks to Robert Temple for his encouragement.

The publishing of this book is possible thanks to the help of my professional partner, Valéry Blandin and also Robin Heath, who despite his own research work, has helped with editing and printing in England. I would also like to thank him for having "re-orientated" me towards Thom's megalithic yard.

To all those nameless beings who took part in the construction of the megalithic sites and who allowed me, many centuries later, to experience the joy of discovery.

Appendices and Tables

Appendix 1 : Convention for describing orientation.

As a general rule orientations are given from the north in a clockwise direction. So East can be written 90°, South 180° and West 270°. In this work I do not respect that convention as it seems to me that the East-West axis, the middle line between the extreme positions of sunrise and sunset at solstice, was the megalithic builders reference. Consequently to express an orientation which is 30° north of the East West axis for example I have written E30°N which means that one turns towards the east and then turns by 30° towards the north.

Appendix 2 : Basic geometry and square roots

The square of a number is the value obtained when a number is multiplied by itself, for example 3 x 3 = 9. The result is always a whole positive number.

The square root of a number, designated by the sign $\sqrt{}$ preceding it, is a value which, when multiplied by itself gives the number, for example $\sqrt{9}$ = 3 because 3 x 3 = 9. The result is not necessarily a whole number and is often an irrational number, meaning that its decimals go on for ever, like the number Pi. This often frightens non mathematicians because of its abstract nature, but in fact a square root can be visualised as the side of a triangle.

For example, $\sqrt{2}$ is the length of the diagonal of a square whose side is 1 unit long.

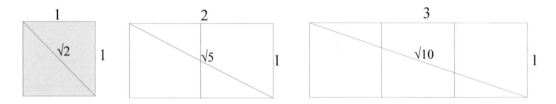

$\sqrt{5}$ is the diagonal of a double square, two equal squares placed side by side, and $\sqrt{10}$ is the diagonal of a triple square. These values can be determined using the theorem of Pythagoras which states that the square of the hypotenuse of a triangle (in this case the diagonal of the rectangle) is equal to the sum of the squares of the other two sides.

$$1^2 + 1^2 = 2, \quad 2^2 + 1^2 = 5, \quad 3^2 + 1^2 = 9 + 1 = 10$$

Many square roots can be expressed to a high degree of accuracy as fractions. For example $\sqrt{2}$ is very close to 99/70, $\sqrt{5}$ approximates to 38/17 and $\sqrt{10}$ to 57/18. So a double square with sides of 17 and 34 units has a diagonal of 38.01 and a triple square with side lengths of 12 and 36 has a diagonal of 37.95. This shows that the use of the measurement of 38my at Le Menec west is very convenient when using double and triple squares!

Appendix 3 : 3+2=1.

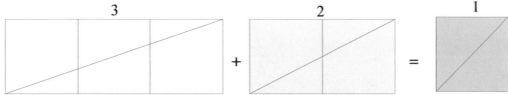

This strange mathematical formula is a short way of saying that if the angle of the diagonal of a triple square is added to the angle of the diagonal of a double square, the result is equal to the angle of the diagonal of a square. Or $18.4349488223° + 26.565051177° = 45°$. This exact relationship between the first three modules, seen in appendix 1 and present in all ancient sacred architecture, is, to my knowledge, unknown to modern science but was central to ancient thinking.

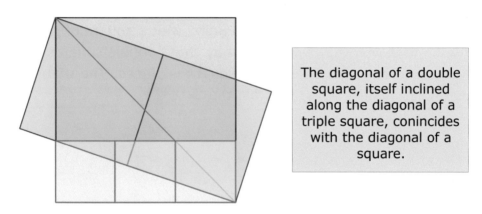

The diagonal of a double square, itself inclined along the diagonal of a triple square, conincides with the diagonal of a square.

The principle of placing one modular form on the diagonal of another to create a third form can be developed in multiple ways.

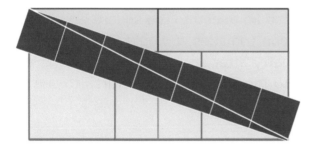

A seven-fold square is placed on the diagonal of a triple square. Its diagonal then coincides with the diagonal of a double square.

I am convinced that this principle is a key to the understanding of many architectural enigmas from the past.

Another expression of the basic relationship of the first three modules is given by the in-circle of a 3-4-5 triangle, which has a radius of 1 unit.

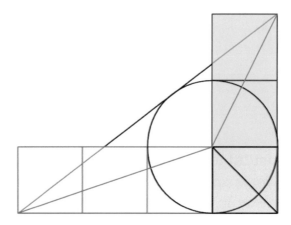

The grey square (on the bottom right) with a side of 1 unit is surmounted by a double square. A triple square is placed beside it. The diagonals of each shape meet at the centre of the circle. They also bisect the angles at each corner of the triangle.

The next in-circle has a radius of two units, with a square of two units in the bottom right corner. It is surmounted by three double squares, giving a 2:3 rectangle. On the right, a quintuple square is placed. The triangle produced is the second triangle of Pythagoras, the 5-12-13.

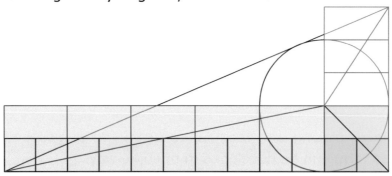

This series is infinite, as one unit can be added to the square each time, and systematically produces Pythagorean triangles. I would like to stress again that I became aware of this geometry after studying the megaliths and did not "project" these principles on to the megalithic structures to see if they "fitted".

Appendix 4 : Pythagorean triangles and their root triangles.

Every Pythagorean triangle can be derived from a basic root triangle which is right angled. Its opposite and adjacent sides (not the hypotenuse) are different whole numbers and its angle is half that of the resulting Pythagorean triangle.

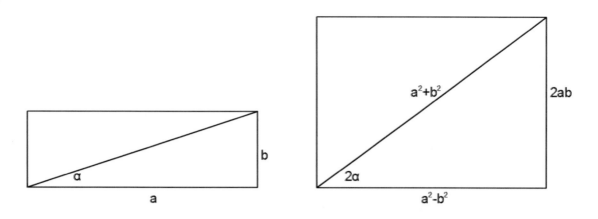

So for the root triangle of the 3-4-5, b=1 and a=3 (a triple square ratio). For the 5-12-13, the root is given by b=1 and a=5 (quintuple square ratio). The next Pythagorean triangle in the series, the 7-24-25 has the root b=1 and a=7 (the septuple square ratio). At Le Menec West, we can clearly identify the use of Pythagorean triangles and their associated root triangle.

Appendix 5 : Joining up the dots to get a triple square angle.

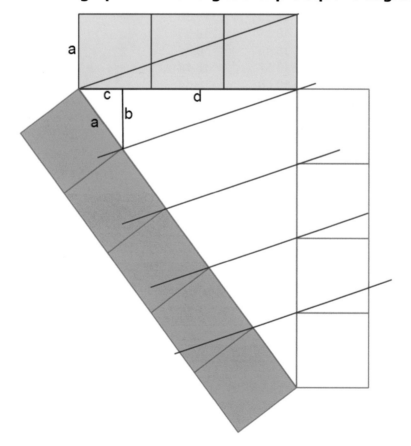

In the above diagram, a 3-4-5 triangle is drawn using squares with a side length a. Mauve lines connect the equal intervals between the 4 side and the 5 side. A line, b, is drawn vertically upwards from the bottom right hand corner of the top square on the 5 side until it reaches the 3 side, thus creating a small 3-4-5 triangle with sides a, b and c.

$c = 3/5 \times a$; $b = 4/5 \times a$; $c + d = 3 \times a$;   so, $d = 3a - 3a/5 = 12a/5$.

As $b = 4a/5$, then $d = 3b$, which is a 1 to 3 relationship.

The mauve lines are consequently parallel to the diagonal of the blue triple square on the 3 side of the triangle.

Table 1 : Thom's survey results for the angles of the rows at Le Menec West

Row	Angle from N	Angle from E	Average
1	251.65	18.35	18.35
2	251.65	18.35	18.35
3	251.65	18.35	18.35
4	251.65	18.35	18.35
5	251.54	18.46	18.37
6	251.43	18.57	18.41
7	251.32	18.68	18.44
8	251.09	18.91	18.5

Table 2 : Square roots and fractions

A series of relationships between square roots, centred around the number 19, is shown in the following table.

	Square	Double	Triple	Quadruple
Diagonal	2	5	10	17
Fraction	99/70	19x2/17	19x3/18	235/3x19

The importance of the quadruple square and the number 235 will be discussed later in volume 2 in the chapter on astronomy.

Table 3 : Thom's survey results for the angles of the rows at Le Menec East

Est

Row	Angle from N	Angle from E	Average
1	65.66	24.34	24.34
2	65.4	24.6	24.47
3	65.14	24.86	24.6
4	64.8	25.2	24.75
5	64.48	25.52	24.9
6	64.16	25.84	25.06
7	63.84	26.16	25.22
8	63.64	26.36	25.36
9	63.45	26.55	25.49
10	63.26	26.74	25.62
11	63.23	26.77	25.72
12	63.19	26.81	25.81

Table 4: Measurements at Newgrange (see Figure 33)

	Units of 2160ft	Feet	Metres	Nautical Miles	my	Units 273.22ft	Units 295.3ft
X1	1.644384	3551.87	1082.61	0.5846	1305.92	13.00000	12.02801
Y1	1.138420	2458.99	749.50	0.4047	904.10	9.00000	8.32708
X2	2.551952	5512.22	1680.12	0.9072	2026.69	20.17495	18.66650
Y2	1.577193	3406.74	1038.37	0.5607	1252.56	12.46881	11.53653
X1+X2	4.196337	9064.09	2762.73	1.4918	3332.61	33.17495	30.69451
Y1+Y2	2.715613	5865.72	1787.87	0.9654	2156.66	21.46881	19.86361
Y2-Y1=h	0.438773	947.75	288.87	0.1560	348.46	3.46881	3.20945
D1	4.219214	9113.5	2777.80	1.4999	3350.78	33.35581	30.86184

Bibliography

[1] Article in the French magazine « Science et Vie », January 2008

[2] Mégalithes, principes de la première architecture monumental du monde, Howard Crowhurst, Editions Epistemea, Plouharnel, France, 2007.

[3]– « Utilisation des mégalithes comme marqueurs de la vitesse de l'érosion des granites en milieu tempéré : enseignements apportés par les alignements de Carnac (Morbihan) », *Zeitschrift für Geomorphologie*, t. 41, n° 3, p. 319-356. Dominique Sellier. 1997

[4] Astronomie Préhistorique, Félix Gaillard, 1895, Reprinted by Epistemea in 2005.

[5] Megalithic remains in Britain and Brittany, Alexander Thom and Archibald Stevenson Thom, Oxford University Press, 1978, reprinted 2003.

[6] Excavations at Carnac (Brittany), James Miln, 1877.

[7] Les Marches du Palais, Serge Cassen, Editions de l'Université de Nantes, 2001

[8] Megalithic sites in Britain, Alexander Thom (Oxford University Press, 1967)

[9] "A Statistical Examination of the Megalithic Sites in Britain". Thom, Alexander (1955). Journal of the Royal Statistical Society.

[10] The Master Masons of Chartres, John James, West Grinstead Publications, London, 1990

[11] All Done with Mirrors, John Neal, The Secret Academy, 2000

[12] L'Architecture cachée, tracés harmoniques; Georges Jouven, Dervy, Paris, 1978.

[13] Issus du Temps, Les Alignements de Carnac, E&T N°10, L'Association Archéologique Kergal, Paris, 1980.

[14] Excavations at Carnac (Brittany), James Miln, 1877. page 66

[15] La Géométrie des alignements de Carnac, Métrologie et astronomie Préhistoriques, A. Thom and A.S. Thom, Université de Rennes, 1977. Journal for the History of Astronomy, vol iii P.11-269, 1972 The Carnac Alignments.

[16] Megalithic remains in Britain and Brittany, page 76

[17] Ancient Metrology, John Michell, Pentacle Books, Bristol, 1981

[18] A travers Carnac d'avant l'histoire, E&T N°9, Association Archéologique Kergal, 1980, p. 52

[19] For additional information see « Alexander Thom, Cracking the Stone Age Code, », Robin Heath, Bluestone Press, bluestonepress@skyhenge.demon.co.uk, 2007.

[20] Issus du Temps, Les alignments de Carnac, E&T N°10, Association Archéologique Kergal, 1980, plan on centre pages.

Made in United States
Troutdale, OR
04/16/2024

19213241R00076